EDIBLE WILD PLANTS

EDIBLE WILD PLANTS

by Oliver Perry Medsger

Professor of Nature Education, Emeritus
The Pennsylvania State College

WITH AN INTRODUCTION BY
Ernest Thompson Seton

Illustrated with Eighty
Pen and Ink Drawings and
Nineteen Photographs

THE MACMILLAN COMPANY
NEW YORK, NEW YORK

Library of Congress catalog card number: 66-23647

EIGHTEENTH PRINTING 1972

INCLUDING NEW INTRODUCTION

The Macmillan Company
866 Third Avenue, New York, N. Y. 10022
Collier-Macmillan Canada Ltd., Toronto, Ontario

Printed in the United States of America

TO MY WIFE

JENNIE ARNOLD MEDSGER

MY COMPANION THROUGH THE
YEARS, THIS VOLUME IS
AFFECTIONATELY DEDICATED

APPRECIATION

WILLIAM C. STEERE

Director, The New York Botanical Garden

THIS book has been an exceptionally durable one, largely because of a certain timeless quality that makes it as useful today as it was when first published, so that its reissue is a natural and highly appropriate event. It has guided several generations of nature lovers to a knowledge of where to find edible plants and what parts of them to eat. As a teacher and field botanist, I have owned and used this book since it first appeared over twenty-five years ago, although my personal enthusiasm for it has occasionally led me astray. I still recall with equal amounts of amusement and embarrassment the repercussions generated by a talk on edible wild plants I gave, innocently enough, on a University of Michigan radio program, just at the end of World War II. For some reason, my remarks were picked up and enlarged upon by the press, and a resourceful reporter who was a family friend telephoned my wife, who hadn't heard the broadcast, to ask if she really cooked skunk-cabbage for me at home. Of course, she indignantly denied it. For weeks, friends widespread over the country kept sending me clipped newspaper items and editorials headlined "Botanist Eats Skunk-Cabbage" and "Botanist's Wife Refuses to Cook Skunk-Cabbage"!

The growing interest in eating wild plants, in part engendered by the first appearance of this book, received a great impetus during World War II. Airborne military personnel who received indoctrination in the use of wild plants for subsistence in the event their planes were downed, as well as civilian families who turned to wild plants during wartime food shortage and rationing, have continued to take advantage of their special knowledge and experience. A further impetus has arisen from the stimulation of interest in plants that grow uncontaminated by man's modern methods of spraying and fertilizing. Sportsmen, hikers, hunters, campers, house-

vii

wives, and everyone who enjoys the outdoors, especially young people, have become even more fascinated by nature and its bountiful gifts.

A beautiful example of the contradiction—if not contrariness—found in nature is the parallel listing of so many kinds of plants in this book on edible plants as well as in books treating those that are poisonous. The handsome red fruit of our wild yew (*Taxus canadensis,* the ground hemlock), and of cultivated yews as well, tastes good and is reasonably safe to eat—but the hard central seed is reputed to be poisonous. Although leaves and young stems of the pokeweed make delicious greens, the root is poisonous. In tropical America, the roots of an enormously productive plant (*Manihot*) variously called mandioca, cassava, and yuca, which is also the source of tapioca, commonly contain cyanic acid and thus may be deadly poisonous when eaten uncooked. Once the root is grated, however, and the poisonous juice squeezed out, the starchy residue becomes a staff of life in the tropics.

In spite of the increasing tempo of interest in edible wild plants in temperate North America, to which this book is devoted, the aboriginal owners of the land, who at one time depended entirely on nature for sustenance, have been largely indoctrinated by the culture we have superimposed upon their own, so that most of the old ways of life have disappeared. Nevertheless, some Indian groups of the southwestern United States still subsist largely on the seeds of the piñon pine, which thus puts them on a feast-or-famine regime, depending on the crop that nature provides. Relatively recently, too, a young Indian, the last member of a small stone-age group that had lived entirely off the country, turned up in central California and became immediately the center of very considerable attention.

It is in the tropics that one finds aboriginal peoples still existing in much their original state, still using their original foods and pharmacopoeia in preference to what the transplanted European culture would have them adopt. In my travels among aboriginal peoples I have been continually astonished at the enormous amount of information they have acquired about the plants that surround them—not the esoteric knowledge possessed by the botanist, but pragmatic and empirical knowledge about the practical uses of plants for food, medicine, and all the other needs of primitive man. "Empirical" is the wholly proper term here, because the uses for so many kinds of plants have been discovered purely by trial and error, under the stresses of hunger, illness, and lack of clothing or shelter, without too much basic curiosity in the direction of what today we call science. One is constantly impressed by the fact that *somebody* has tried *everything!* Every plant, whether poisonous or not, has been sampled for food, medicine, or other purposes. Those who succumbed to the poisonous ones must have been able to indicate the cause of their final agony, to the ultimate and permanent benefit of the tribe, although at the expense of the individual. In the Americas, every group of Indians that has not yet been exposed too closely to the corner grocery or drug store has amassed an impressive folklore knowledge of local edible, poisonous, and medicinal plants—the latter more often drawn from the poisonous ones than not. We must remember that aboriginal Americans discovered not only the potato and maize, but also tobacco, cascara sagrada, coca, quinine, ipecac, strychnine, and many other drugs which are still important in modern medicine.

An American visiting the market places of mountain villages in Guatemala, for example, will have a somewhat disquieting sensation that our "civilization" has not really replaced the original way of life of a very large proportion of the population—and that in some ways perhaps we are the losers.

One factor we tend to forget amid our modern and enlightened age is that literateness tends to erode memory. One who can write does so and later refers to his notes instead of his memory. By our standards, illiterate peoples have prodigious memories—their voluminous folklore is committed to memory by their leaders, the medicine men, the shamans, and the midwives, for example.

Every one of us, whether he wishes to admit it or not, has descended (I wonder why Darwin used that word!) from aboriginal peoples who lived entirely off the land, at first without the luxury of fire. The manner of life, meaning basically the food habits, can be determined by inspecting their remains, principally the skull of primitive man. If his teeth are practically worn off, he was used to eating raw plants full of abrasive materials, whereas teeth in relatively good condition indicate a higher cultural level, showing that he ate cooked plants, after the "discovery" of fire. The astonishing thing is how really brief is the history of man, and how rapidly he has adjusted to changing conditions in his environment, to the point that now his environment is being drastically—if not catastrophically—changed by him.

Because of man's recent emergence as an organism that can determine its way of life and overcome some of the pressures of environment, he still has a strong atavistic pressure from his past. Our urge to dig up young and succulent dandelions in the spring, to scrounge "wild" asparagus along roadsides, and to make jams and jellies from wild fruits is usually ascribed to our recent pioneer background—but I am sure that it goes back much further, to innate instincts developed when our forebears either lived off the land or starved to death. Thus, this book, in addition to providing much useful and interesting information, also appeals to a fundamental human drive.

January, 1966

INTRODUCTION

BY

Ernest Thompson Seton

More than once I have been called to write the introduction to a book treating on some aspect of nature that was much in the line of my own interests; and usually had no difficulty in penning the few pages that were called for. But the introduction to a book by Oliver P. Medsger proved a wholly different undertaking.

Why this should be the case will be better understood when I describe my first meeting with this man of the woods.

It was at Woodland, New York, in the camp of Harry Little (Sagamore), that my good luck sent me out on a forest walk with Medsger; and every yard of our trip was made delightful by some bit of information about the myriad forms of wild life around us —forms with which I had been superficially acquainted all my life, but which I never really knew, because I had no exact names, no knowledge of their virtues.

It reminded me of an incident in my early life in the West. A prairie-born girl was asked by her mother what her dream of heaven would be. The child's whole life had been in the home circle on the Plains; so she said simply: "Heaven is a place with a big shady tree, and an angel sitting under it, who never says, 'I don't know,' when asked a question."

In my own childhood and youth, I suffered beyond expression from the knowledge-hunger, from the impossibility of learning about the abounding wild life around me. And now, when it seemed almost too late, I had found a competent guide. I know now why his Indian name is "Nibowaka," the "Wise Woodman."

"This man has opened and read the book of nature," I said. "And, more than that, he loves it, for his knowledge embodies not only the names and qualities of the plants and trees, but also the poetical ideas about them, and pleasant little rhymes and fancies that fix the bird or flower in memory and give it the romantic glamour so vital to the lover of the woods."

That walk was one of many in the years that followed; and the joy of the first was not exceptional. The qualities of his talk were the same—a mingling of science and art, encyclopedic information and romantic joy in the woodland world of beauty.

Thus you see why I was possessed of a sense of being over-whelmed when confronted with the responsibility of writing this introduction. As a matter of fact, I made many attempts during the last year, and cast each aside in turn.

But the book is in press, I must keep faith with the printer.

If an introduction is meant to be an adequate proclamation to the world of a new arrival among its books of worth, then I must put this also in the fire and give up the attempt. But I am in hopes that it will serve, if only to announce to all the heart-hungry forest folk that here is the book I longed for so much in my youth—here is the angel of the prairie girl. I know it will serve the coming wood-wanderers as it would have served me. It will be the book I dreamed of—the key to the woods.

FOREWORD

MORE than thirty years ago, I was with Dr. Harvey M. Hall when he made his botanical survey of San Jacinto Mountain, California. An intelligent Indian joined us for a few days and acted as guide. He was much interested in the plants used by the American Indians, especially those used for food. After I came East, for several years we exchanged specimens and seeds. I sent the Indian nuts of nearly all the edible nut-bearing species in northeastern United States, also acorns, seeds of edible berries, and those of other wild fruits. These he planted along canyons and in moist situations where he thought they might grow.

From that time on I have collected data on edible plants from books, published reports, papers, from the experiences of people, and wherever information on the subject could be obtained. When possible, I observed the trees or plants first hand, often experimenting or testing out their edible qualities.

This manual does not include all the edible plants in this country. A few were omitted intentionally because of their rarity or limited range, others because their edible qualities were not well known or defined. The reader will probably recall other species not mentioned here simply because we have not learned that they could be eaten. I hope at least that this publication will be found useful and serve as a basis for future investigations on the edible plants of the United States.

In certain large groups, such as the blackberries, the blueberries or huckleberries, and the serviceberries, I have described only a few important species and referred to the others as having similar edible qualities, or being used for the same or similar purposes.

If anyone doubts that wild vegetable foods were important to the pioneers or to the American Indians, let him read the Journals of Lewis and Clark in their expedition across the continent, 1804–1806, or that of Henry Schoolcraft among the Indians of the Northwest a few years later. Many books have been written on our American game animals, but I cannot recall a single volume devoted exclusively to the wild vegetable foods of the United States, giving descriptions of the plants and telling how they are used. Harvard University published a bulletin or report on the food plants of the American Indians, which is brief and quite incomplete. Dr. Charles F. Saunders, in his *Useful Wild Plants* mentions very few edible species of the Northeast. Dr. Edward L. Sturtevant in his *Notes on Edible Plants* refers to species in this country and abroad, but he rarely describes them.

Many of my naturalist friends have expressed the thought that their interest in botany and in nature, generally, was first aroused when they were boys on excursions to the fields and woods, in search of wild fruits and nuts. The experience is akin to hunting and fishing. Who could pluck the ripe May Apple without becoming interested in the plant that produced it, or sample the spicy Partridge berries without making note of where and how the plants grew and when the fruit ripened?

The more important edible wild plants are described here, but at the end of each chapter there is a list of others not so well known; or, at least, their edible qualities have not been so well tested. Some of these probably should have been given more attention.

In general I have followed the International System of Nomenclature, but where so many references have been consulted, mistakes in scientific names are sure to occur. Synonyms are given where it seems necessary.

In this volume are described species from nearly all of the chief orders of flowering plants, as well as a few lower forms of plant life, covering the entire United States and Canada. A key including such a wide range of vegetation would necessarily be very complicated—too long and complex for the average reader, and of little use to a botanist. In place of a key, we have substituted a "finding index" which gives the names of plants, both common and scientific, with the range, season, and a few of the most pronounced characteristics. We hope this index will prove of some value, especially in determining those plants mentioned but not described near the end of each chapter. For further technical descriptions of these plants, the reader should consult a good manual of botany covering his particular region.

I wish to thank all those who have aided me in the preparation of this volume, either by giving definite information or by sending specimens, and I especially wish to thank George A. King, naturalist and artist, for his valuable suggestions and for the care with which he has prepared the drawings; also my wife, Jennie Arnold Medsger, who helped to test the edible qualities of many of the plants described here.

The author is pleased to acknowledge his indebtedness to various works of reference and their publishers: Bailey's *Standard Cyclopedia of Horticulture and Camping and Woodcraft*, by Horace Kephart (published by the Macmillan Company); Britton and Brown's *Illustrated Flora of the United States and Canada*, and *Our Native Trees*, by Harriet Keeler (Charles Scribner's Sons); Gray's *New Manual of Botany* (American Book Company); *Flora of the Southeastern United States*, by J. K. Small; *Manual of the Flowering Plants of California*, by Willis Linn Jepson, copyright by the author; *The Flora of New Mexico*, by Wooton and Standley, Smithsonian Institution; publications of the United States Department of Agriculture and the Bureau of American Ethnology; *A Yosemite Flora*, by Dr. Harvey M. Hall; *Handbook of Trees*, by Romeyn B. Hough.

I wish especially to thank Doubleday, Doran and Co. for allowing me to quote from *The Tree Book* and *Book of Useful Plants*, by Julia E. Rogers, *Nature's Garden*, by Neltje Blanchan, and *Orchard and Fruit Garden*, by E. P. Powell; also Robert M. McBride & Co. for excerpts from *Useful Wild Plants of the United States and Canada*, by Dr. Charles F. Saunders, and the New York Agricultural Experiment Station for the privilege of quoting from Dr. Edward L. Sturtevant's *Notes on Edible Plants;* Houghton, Mifflin Co. for quotations from Warner's *My Summer in a Garden* and Burroughs's *Bird and Bough;* Little, Brown and Company, for excerpts from *Trees and Shrubs of Massachusetts*, by G. B. Emerson; the J. B. Lippincott Company for a quotation from *Recent Rambles*, by Dr. Charles C. Abbott; Ernest Thompson Seton for a quotation from the *Boys' Manual of Woodcraft* and William Hamilton Gibson, for an excerpt from the writing of his father.

I am grateful to the authors and their publishers for various poetical quotations, credit for which is given in footnotes, and to Frederick Warne and Company for the use of photographs for halftones which I had previously reproduced in *Nature Rambles*.

CONTENTS

ILLUSTRATIONS

Following page 168

Edible Morel (Morchella esculenta var. conica)

Yucca-Southern Texas, probably Yucca Treculeana

Mandrake or May Apple (Podophyllum peltatum)

Wild or Scarlet Strawberry (Fragaria virginiana)

Blackberry

American Cranberry (Vaccinium macrocarpon)

California Fan Palm (Washingtonia filifera)

Nest of the pack rat in New Mexico

Black Locust (Robinia Pseudo-Acacia)

Palmetto or Cabbage Palm (Sabal Palmetto)

Skunk Cabbage (Symplocarpus fotidus)

Common Poke or Pigeonberry (Phytolacca decandra)

Common Milkweed (Asclepias syriaca)

Arrowhead or Wapatoo (Sagittaria latifolia)

Prairie Apple or Indian Breadroot (Psoralea esculenta)

Wild Potato-vine or Mecha-meck (Ipomoea pandurata)

Black or Cherry Birch (Betula lenta)

Balsam Fir (Abies balsamea)

Oyster Mushroom (Pleurotus ostreatus)

EDIBLE WILD PLANTS

EDIBLE WILD FRUITS

O,—fruit loved of boyhood!—the old days recalling,
When wood-grapes were purpling and brown nuts were falling!
—J. G. WHITTIER

AMERICA is blessed with wild fruits. It would be difficult to find a piece of woodland or an abandoned field that did not some time during the season produce one or more species of wild fruits that are edible raw or could be prepared in some way for the table. Blackberries, blueberries, plums, and wild grapes often grow in rank profusion, and country people frequently make great use of them. Some of our finest horticultural varieties have been developed from native wild species. Others yet untamed have great possibilities and it is hoped that man some day will apply the factors of evolution to their development.

Thoreau once wrote: "It takes a savage or wild taste to appreciate a wild fruit." Boys possess this taste to a marked degree and even seem to relish green apples and chokecherries. But many wild fruits have a delicacy of flavor scarcely approached by horticultural varieties. In some cases, as in the development of the strawberry, flavor has been sacrificed for size, beauty, and texture.

The following list does not contain all the species of edible berries of the United States. Other species of blackberries and blue or huckleberries have been described by botanists, but often the distinguishing features between species are not well marked; and for our purpose we need not attempt to discriminate between them. It is well to know that they are edible and wholesome, and the joy of gathering and eating them may be ours.

AMERICAN YEW, OR GROUND HEMLOCK

Taxus canadensis

THE American Yew is a low spreading evergreen shrub, from one to four feet high, much resembling a small hemlock, especially one that has been smashed to the ground. The leaves resemble those

1

of the hemlock in arrangement and appearance, but are larger with sharp points. They are dark green above and below.

The blossoms are generally dioecious—that is, the staminate and pistillate are on separate bushes. The fruit is an oblong, bright red fleshy cup, with the hard dark brown naked seed at the bottom.

American Yew (Taxus canadensis)

This shrub is found in damp shady woods from Newfoundland to Manitoba, south to New Jersey and Iowa, and in the mountains to Virginia.

The beautiful red fleshy berry, about one-third of an inch long, is sweet but slightly resinous. They are never very abundant, but it is usually not desirable to eat many at a time. In walking through our northern woods in July and August, I often gather and eat a few of these berries when I happen to come across them. The fruit frequently clings to the branches until winter. Do not chew or swallow the seeds as they may be poisonous.

SPANISH BAYONET, OR SPANISH DAGGER

Yucca baccata

THE Spanish Bayonet is a semidesert plant growing on tablelands and rocky ridges from Colorado to western Nevada, south into Mexico, extending east to Texas and west to California. It is low or almost stemless, leafy to the base. The leaves are stiff and sharp-pointed, one to three feet long.

From the center of the leafy mass arises a panicle with numerous white bell-shaped blossoms two or three inches across. The edible fruit or seed pod is large and pulpy, three to six inches long. It has been compared to a short or stubby banana. The fruit when ripe has been described as dark purple, also yellow. Probably two species have been confused in botanical descriptions. The Mexicans speak of the plant as *dátil,* or "date fruit." Wooton and Standley in their *Flora of New Mexico* say of this species: "The fruit, too, is characteristic, somewhat resembling the eastern pawpaw in general appearance. The Indians of New Mexico slice the ripe fruit and dry it in the sun for use in winter. When fresh, it has a peculiar sweet taste and is quite palatable."

Charles F. Saunders, who was an eyewitness to the roasting of the green fruits of this species in their campfires by the Indian women of Arizona says: "I can testify to the entire palatability of this cooked fruit (the rind being first removed), finding it pleasantly suggestive of sweet potato." Dr. Henry H. Rusby told Dr. Saunders that the sliced pulp of the nearly ripe pods makes a pie that is scarcely distinguishable from apple pie. The Indians sometimes ate the fruit fresh, but it was generally cooked or roasted. They also ate the young flower buds of this and other species of yucca after they were cooked. The seed pod may be gathered in summer and autumn.

I have collected the seed pods of several species of yucca from California to Texas and find that the fruits are apt to be infested with the larva of the moth that fertilizes the blossoms. The fleshy-fruited species are apparently less affected than the others.

Adam's Needle, or Bear Grass (Yucca glauca), found from South Dakota and Montana south to Texas and Arizona, has a less pulpy seed pod than the last species. Its pods were also gathered and cooked by the Indians, especially when food was scarce. Fruit ripe in autumn.

The seed pods of the common Yucca, or Adam's Needle, also called Eve's Darning Needle (Yucca filamentosa), was also sometimes eaten by the Indians. It is native from Maryland to Tennessee, south to Florida and Louisiana, and has escaped from cultivation farther north. Late summer and autumn is the time to collect this wild fruit.

The Broad-Leaved Yucca, Yucca macrocarpa, has rather large fruits that are slightly pulpy and are sometimes cooked by the Indians. It is a tall species common from western Texas to California.

HACKBERRY, OR SUGARBERRY
Celtis occidentalis

HACKBERRIES are rare in some localities and quite common in others, yet I find that they are generally not well known. There seem to be several species in this country, but many of their characteristics are much alike; and they so intergrade that even botanists have much trouble in distinguishing them.

This hackberry varies from a small tree to a tree two or three feet in diameter. The bark is very hard, rough, and corky or warty. The leaves, like those of the elm, are unequal-sided, with long points and saw-tooth edges, smooth above and downy beneath. The small greenish flowers have a four- or five-lobed calyx but no corolla. They appear in the axils of the leaves. The staminate blossoms are

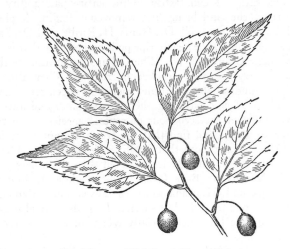

Hackberry (Celtis occidentalis)

clustered; the pistillate are less numerous and occur singly or two or three together.

The fruit is a fleshy drupe from a fourth to a third of an inch in diameter, nearly round, orange-brown or purplish, with a rather large round seed. The pulpy covering is very sweet and pleasant to the taste.

This tree grows in dry, often rocky soil, from Quebec to North Carolina, west to Manitoba and Oklahoma. It is quite common on the dry creek and river hills of western Pennsylvania, West Virginia, and Ohio. The berries are ripe in September but hang on the trees all winter and are greatly relished by many of our winter birds.

When I was a lad in western Pennsylvania, I often took excursions for sugarberries, with my companions. We frequently returned, each with a pint of berries in his coat pockets, and enjoyed eating them, especially when seated around a campfire into which we threw the seeds, which explode with a popping sound.

The Western, or Thick-Leaved, Hackberry (Celtis reticulata), is found from western Kansas and Colorado south and west to Texas, California, and Mexico. It is not a large tree but is used for street planting in the cities and towns of New Mexico, occasionally reaching a foot in diameter and forty feet in height. The leaves are smaller and thicker than those of the eastern species. The fruits seem to vary greatly in color, and botanists have described them as ranging from orange-red to blue. Those that I examined in New Mexico were brown. In *Flora of New Mexico* Wooton and Standley state: "The berries of this tree are edible and were often eaten by the Indians." They are ripe in late summer and autumn.

The Southern Hackberry, Celtis mississippiensis, is a large forest tree common in the southern states. It is much planted along streets and in parks of our southern cities. The fruits, although edible, are generally small with very little pulp.

ROUGH-LEAVED HACKBERRY
Celtis crassifolia

THIS is the largest of our hackberries, attaining a diameter of four feet or more, and sometimes reaching a height of nearly a hundred feet. It is in many respects much like the former species. The bark is thick and rough. The young twigs are downy, and the leaves are rough, hairy above, and downy or rough beneath. The nearly round fruits are about three-eighths of an inch in diameter, nearly black, and sweet, ripe in autumn.

This tree is found in low rich grounds and river bottoms from Massachusetts to South Carolina, west to Tennessee, Kansas, and South Dakota. It apparently reaches its highest development in the Ohio valley.

A tree of this species well known to my boyhood stood by the roadside about two hundred yards from the mouth of Jacobs Creek in Westmoreland County, Pennsylvania. It resembled a large spreading elm—a beautiful tree with purplish black fruits. In the summer of 1916, I made a trip to the spot to photograph the tree and collect specimens from it, but to my great regret, found that it had just been cut down "because it shaded the road." The

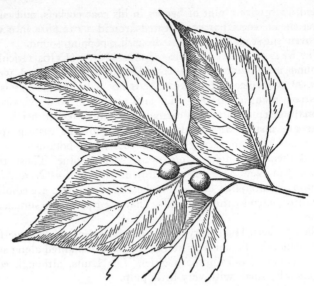

Rough-Leaved Hackberry (Celtis crassifolia)

stump, two feet from the ground, measured four feet six inches in diameter. The rings of growth indicated that it was growing rapidly.

RED MULBERRY
Morus rubra

THIS tree sometimes grows to a diameter of three or four feet and a height of fifty to sixty feet, with a spreading, branching top. The bark is dark grayish brown or reddish brown, splitting into irregular plates. The alternate leaves are variable like those of the Sassafras. Some are broadly oval, others are mitten-shaped or with three to five lobes. The edges are coarsely toothed. The upper surface is rough, and the under surface is covered with downy hairs. The greenish flowers appear in the axils of the leaves in the form of catkinlike spikes. The staminate and pistillate blossoms are in separate spikes but generally on the same tree. If a tree bears only staminate blossoms, of course it will produce no fruit. The berries are formed of numerous drupelets making a fleshy fruit from three-fourths of an inch to an inch and a half long. As they ripen, they take on a bright red hue; but when fully ripe, which is generally in July, they are dark purple. They are delicious and may be eaten fresh with sugar and cream or made into pies or jam.

The Red Mulberry is found from western New England to Michigan and South Dakota, south to Florida and Texas. It delights in rich soil and perhaps reaches its greatest development in the Ohio valley.

I have never understood just why authors speak of the fruit of this tree as insipid. It is certainly among the most pleasing of all

Red Mulberry (Morus rubra)

our wild fruits. I recall the delightful walks taken with companions in search of mulberries. When the trees were large, the fruits were generally shaken to the ground, for as Dinah Maria Muloch says:

> While far overhead hang gorgeously
> Large luscious berries of sanguine dye,
> For the best grows highest, always highest,
> Upon the mulberry tree.

I recall a tree—not a large one—from which we gathered a gallon of delicious berries at one time. They were exceptionally large and juicy, dyeing our hands and lips with deep purple. This tree was worthy of cultivation, in fact, there are several cultivated forms of our native mulberry.

WHITE MULBERRY
Morus alba

Two hundred years ago, when silk culture was first attempted in the United States, the White Mulberry, a native of China, was introduced into this country from Europe. The various attempts at silk culture proved a failure, chiefly because of high labor cost,

White Mulberry (Morus alba)

but the White Mulberry remained with us. It has escaped to road-sides, fence rows, and waste lands generally, being most abundant east of the Appalachian Mountains from Maine to Florida, but has gone west as far as Minnesota and Texas. It is rare west of the mountains.

This tree attains a diameter of from one to three feet. The rough bark is gray, and the branches are grayish yellow. The leaves are light green, thin, ovate, or sometimes lobed and divided, with coarse-toothed edges.

The fruit is half an inch to an inch long, white, sometimes pink-purple, not so juicy as the Red Mulberry, very sweet, but somewhat insipid. It is greatly liked by birds and generally by boys. The so-called Russian Mulberry of the nurserymen is a form of this species. The fruit is ripe from June to August.

The Black Mulberry, Morus nigra, a native of western Asia and eastern Europe, has been introduced from New York to Florida and has sparingly escaped from cultivation. It is not hardy north. The rather large black berries are very sweet and pleasant. It has long been cultivated in Europe for its fruit.

A small native species, Morus microphylla, is found from Texas to Arizona and in northern Mexico. The red fruit is described as "palatable when ripe, having a pleasant acid flavor."

PAPAW, OR CUSTARD APPLE, OR FALSE BANANA

Asimina triloba

THE Papaw tree has the appearance of being an escape from the tropics which it really is, for all the other members of the Custard Apple family are tropical. Like many of the smaller trees near the equator, it grows in the shade, but usually where the woods are

American Papaw (Asimina triloba)

somewhat open. Its preferred habitat is in rich soil along streams where it often forms thickets.

This small tree grows from ten to forty feet high and generally not more than six inches in diameter. It is often shrublike. The large alternate, smooth leaves are from six inches to a foot long. They are dark green above, lighter beneath, with entire margins.

They taper toward the base and are attached to the twigs by short petioles.

The flowers appear with the leaves late in April or early in May. They develop in the axils of the last year's leaves. The blossoms, about an inch and a half in diameter, have six petals in two sets The three inner ones are smaller and more erect than the three forming the outer circle. The flowers are at first green but later become a reddish purple.

The fruits when mature resemble stubby bananas often four or five inches long and more than an inch and a half thick. When ripe, they are greenish yellow, turning brown a few days after they are pulled. The sweet edible pulp is bright yellow and surrounds the large brown seeds. James Whitcomb Riley, in his Hoosier dialect, well describes this wild fruit:

> And sich pop-paws!—Lumps o' raw
> Gold and green,—jes' oozy th'ough
> With ripe yaller—like you've saw
> Custard-pie with no crust to.[1]

The papaw is native from New Jersey to Michigan and Nebraska, south to Florida and Texas. It probably reaches its highest development in the Ohio and Mississippi valleys. The fruit is ripe in late autumn.

We find recorded a great difference of opinion as to the edible qualities of this wild fruit. Harriet L. Keeler in "Our Native Trees" says, "Although credited in the books as edible and wholesome, one must be either very young or very hungry really to enjoy its flavor."

In Romeyn B. Hough's *Handbook of the Trees* we find recorded: "The fruit when ripe is delicious and nutritious." I would agree with Dr. Hough. Boys generally do not relish it. Like many tropical fruits, we must apparently learn to enjoy it. In my own experience as a boy, I disliked it; but I kept on trying, and in a few years no other wild fruit appealed to me more. I enjoy it today. I had the same experience with ripe figs eaten fresh from the tree. I have friends that have gone through the same experience with the papaw. I have helped to gather a peck of this wild fruit at one time, and we could have gathered a bushel. If they were not quite ripe, we put them into the haymow or bran bin to mellow. It is believed

[1] From "Armazindy" by James Whitcomb Riley, copyright 1894–1922. Used by special permission of the publishers, The Bobbs-Merrill Co.

that the American Indians made much use of this wild fruit. The generic name *Asimina* came from the Indian.

I have seen papaws in the New York markets and at the fruit stalls of other cities; but for market purposes they are generally pulled before they are quite ripe, and then they are not so delicious.

On the return journey of Lewis and Clark, when they had reached western Missouri, game was scarce, each man was allowed only one biscuit a day; but an abundance of papaws grew on the banks of the river and supplied them with nourishing food.

The Pond Apple, Annona glabra, native of the marsh lands of southern Florida and the Bahama Islands, is also a member of the Custard Apple family. This small tree bears a fruit about five inches long, yellowish blotched with brown when ripe. It is somewhat insipid but is used for making jellies. Some cultivated forms are said to be excellent. The Seminole Indians made much use of this fruit.

The Soursop, Annona muricata, a native of the West Indies, is similar to the Pond Apple and belongs to the same family. It is often sold in the southern markets and is used in making jellies and conserves.

The Sweetsop, or Sugar Apple (Annona squamosa), native of tropical America, is quite similar to the Soursop but much sweeter. Its fruit is used in sherbets and for jellies and preserves.

The Papaya, Carica Papaya, often called the Custard Apple or Papaw, belongs to an entirely different family (Papaya). It is native of southern Florida and the tropics. It is cultivated in warm regions for its large sweet fruit. Two varieties grow wild in Florida.

BARBERRY

Berberis vulgaris

THE Barberry, a native of Europe and Asia, has been thoroughly naturalized in the eastern and middle states, especially in New England. This shrub grows six or eight feet high, with slender arched or drooping gray branches. The alternate or fascicled leaves are an inch to an inch and a half long, rounded at the apex, tapering at the base, bristly, and sawtoothed. Three-pronged spines take the place of leaves on many of the younger shoots. The pale yellow flowers are arranged in drooping racemes. Each blossom is about a quarter of an inch in diameter. The orange-red or scarlet berries, ripe in September, hang in dense, elongated racemes. The berries are about half an inch long, edible but sour.

The barberry grows in thickets, along roadsides and in waste places. In cultivation there are many forms. A yellow dye is ob-

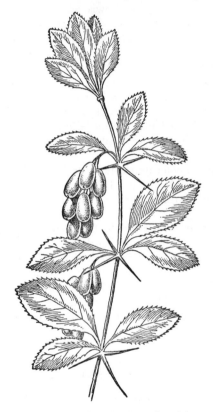

Barberry (Berberis vulgaris)

tained from the bark of the root. The berries are often used for preserves and jellies. Friends of the writer prefer jelly made from the barberry to that produced from any other fruit. The berries are sometimes used for making pies.

The American Barberry (Berberis canadensis), a native shrub similar to the species described above, grows along the mountains from Virginia to Georgia. The bushes are smaller and the berries fewer, shorter and more oval than those of the European species. The fruits of the American barberry are also used for the making of jelly. They are ripe in early autumn.

MAY APPLE, OR MANDRAKE, OR WILD LEMON
Podophyllum peltatum

THIS beautiful but ill-smelling plant of the Barberry family grows in dense patches along fences, roadsides, and in open woods. It pushes through the ground in early spring, its leaves unfolding like a tiny umbrella. The long horizontal rootstalks are poisonous and remain in the ground year after year, sending up each spring a one or two-leaved plant from twelve to eighteen inches high. If the plant has but one leaf, the stem is attached to the center. The single leaf is nearly a foot in diameter, shield-shaped with five to nine lobes. The plants that bear but a single leaf do not produce blossoms. The flowering stems fork near the top, having a pair of similar leaves somewhat smaller and attached near the inner edges. The waxy, ill-smelling nodding flower, nearly two inches in diameter, appears from the fork or axil of the leaves. It has from six to nine pure white petals with double as many stamens. The edible fruit, which is ripe in July or August, is about two inches long, egg-shaped, yellow, with a many-seeded pulp within a rather tough skin.

The May Apple is native from Quebec to Florida, west to Minnesota, Kansas, and Texas. I have observed that west of the Appalachian Mountains the plants and fruits are generally larger than they are farther east. The fruits are best for eating when the plants are dying and falling to the ground. Then they are fully ripe and almost a golden yellow. James Whitcomb Riley, the poet, has well described the fruit of this plant:

> And will any poet sing
> Of a lusher, richer thing
> Than a ripe May-apple, rolled
> Like a pulpy lump of gold
> Under thumb and finger-tips,
> And poured molten through the lips? [1]

[1] From "Rhymes of Childhood" by James Whitcomb **Riley, copyright** 1890, 1918. Used by special permission of the publishers, **The Bobbs-Merrill Company.**

Asa Gray maligns this excellent wild fruit when he says it is "slightly acid, mawkish, eaten by pigs and boys." I like better the description given by Gray's leading contemporary, Alphonso Wood, who writes, "Fruit ovoid-oblong, large, yellowish, with the flavor of the strawberry." In regard to things to eat, boys are generally more discriminating than grown people. They eat fewer things but have a natural appetite for wild fruit. Nearly all boys are fond of May Apples, but the appetite for this particular wild fruit seems to leave one at the approach of manhood. I can eat them yet, but not with the relish of youth.

May Apples should be eaten in moderation. I vividly recall an experience of my own when I was a small boy perhaps eight years old. One afternoon in August my parents went to a neighbor's for a few hours leaving a brother who was three years older than I, at home with me with instructions not to get into mischief. We went down a lane to a large open woods where thousands of May Apples were at their very best. Some were nearly as large as the eggs of a chicken. We filled our hats to overflowing, then sat under a tree near the house to enjoy them. They were delicious, and it was the first time that I could eat all the May Apples that I wanted and not have someone around to say "no." Half an hour later I was rolling on the ground with the worst colic that one could imagine. I felt certain that I was going to die but hoped to put off the fatal moment until my parents returned. An hour or two later the discomfort left me without any ill effects; but I shall never forget the agonizing experience.

RED GARDEN CURRANT
Ribes vulgare

THE Garden Currant with its nearly erect branches, almost smooth, three- to five-lobed leaves, and racemes of yellowish green flowers followed by plump juicy berries, red when mature, has escaped to fence rows, open woods, and thickets from Massachusetts to Virginia, and west to Wisconsin; also in Oregon and Washington.

This shrub, a native of Europe, and commonly planted in gardens is familiar to all. The berries range from a quarter to a third of an inch in diameter and are famous for pies and jellies. Uncultivated plants generally bear smaller and fewer berries than plants growing in a garden.

AMERICAN RED CURRANT, OR SWAMP RED CURRANT

Ribes triste

THIS is a low shrub with reclining branches which often take root. The leaves, three- to five-lobed, are very similar to those of the Garden Currant. They are smooth above and white woolly or downy beneath. In the southern part of its range, the leaves are nearly smooth beneath. The grayish brown or purplish flowers, in racemes, are borne on the old wood. The smooth red berries, about a quarter of an inch in diameter, are quite firm and sour. They are ripe in midsummer.

This currant is found in wet woods and bogs from Newfoundland to Alaska, south to New England, Michigan, and South Dakota. The fruit is of value for pies and jellies.

FETID CURRANT, OR SKUNK CURRANT

Ribes prostratum

Ribes glandulosum

THIS native shrub spreads its light brown, almost straw-colored branches on the ground. The nearly round heart-shaped leaves nave from five to seven lobes. The racemes of greenish flowers stand erect. The red berries, about a quarter of an inch in diameter, contain a few glandular bristles or hairs.

The plant is found from Newfoundland to British Columbia, south to New England, Michigan, and Minnesota, and along the mountains to North Carolina. When handled or bruised it emits a disagreeable odor. The berries are of a peculiar taste and somewhat sour. I recall a very warm July day when I was in the midst of a large forest in the Catskill Mountains, studying the plant life of the region. I became very thirsty, but water was not handy. I collected and ate the fruits of this currant. They quenched my thirst, satisfied my hunger, and in all were not unpleasant.

WILD BLACK CURRANT

Ribes floridum

Ribes americanum

THIS erect shrub grows three to five feet high. The leaves are sharply three- to five-lobed, each lobe with doubly serrate teeth. The flowers, arranged in a raceme, are yellowish white. They appear with the same buds as the leaves. The shining black berries, when ripe, are nearly round, smooth, and from a quarter to a third of an inch in diameter. They are used for pies and jellies but have a peculiar flavor disliked by many persons; others are fond of them. They ripen in summer. This currant is found from New Brunswick to Manitoba and southward.

The Black Currant of the garden, Ribes nigrum, a native of Europe, is very similar to the American species described above. The wild species is rarely cultivated, but occasionally the European species escapes to thickets and woods.

MISSOURI, GOLDEN, OR BUFFALO CURRANT

Ribes aureum

Ribes odoratum

THE Golden Currant is a native shrub found from Minnesota to Texas west to Washington and California, but is frequently cultivated throughout the East as an ornamental shrub and sometimes escapes to waste lands and woods.

It grows from four to eight feet high with slender curving branches. The leaves taper to the base that is broadly wedge-shaped, and have three cut-toothed lobes. The flowers, which appear early in May, are arranged in short racemes with leafy bracts. The blossoms are almost an inch long, golden yellow with a pleasing spicy odor; hence the common name of Clove Bush.

The fruit is black, occasionally yellow, with rather an insipid flavor. The bushes apparently do not bear well in the East, probably because of the lack of proper insects to pollinate the blossoms. Some people enjoy the fruit, but it is disagreeable to others. Good pies and jellies are made from it. The Crandall, a form cultivated for its fruit, was developed from this species. Both the cultivated and wild varieties differ wonderfully as to the size and quality of the berries.

The Golden Currant was first collected by Captain Lewis, on the Lewis and Clark Expedition across the continent in 1805. He apparently found it along the headwaters of both the Missouri and

Golden Currant (Ribes aureum)

the Columbia River. Several times in their Journal, they speak of feasting on wild currants.

The Indians used dried currants for the making of pemmican— a food produced by pounding together dried buffalo meat and fruit then mixed in fat or tallow. The mass was then formed into loaves or cakes and could be transported on long journeys.

WILD, OR PRICKLY, GOOSEBERRY
Ribes Cynosbati
Grossularia Cynosbati

THE Prickly Wild Gooseberry is a graceful shrub three or four feet high with long drooping branches. The leaves, which are from one to two inches broad, nearly round as to general outline with from three to five lobes, and a heart-shaped base, are generally in clusters of three or four with one or more prickles or spines near the base of each cluster. There are also a few spines along the twigs and branches. From one to three greenish flowers appear in the same cluster with the leaves. The brownish red or purplish berries, about half an inch in diameter, are generally armed with numerous prickles, but sometimes are nearly smooth. They ripen in July and August and are pleasantly flavored.

This shrub is found in rocky woods from Maine to North Carolina and Alabama, west to Manitoba and Missouri. The bushes vary wonderfully as to the size and quality of the fruit. They generally do best where they can get some sunshine. I have never

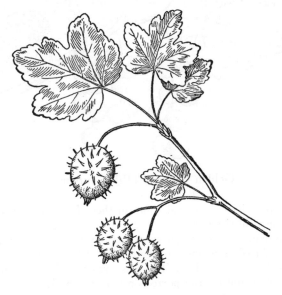

Wild Gooseberry (Ribes Cynosbati)

found the wild gooseberry larger or better than in the Allegheny plateau in western Pennsylvania and West Virginia. The Mountain Gooseberry, a cultivated variety, was developed from this species.

On account of the prickly character of the berries, they have to be eaten with care; but when ripe they are pleasant, and the subacid quality makes them especially desirable for quenching thirst.

This wild fruit is excellent for pies, jellies, and preserves. I have gathered the berries by the quart and can testify as to their merit. Gooseberry pie was famous in colonial times.

Julia E. Rogers in her *Book of Useful Plants* says:

We who have picked the small, but sprightly, green gooseberries
of the woods, both the prickly and the smooth ones, know that no
cultivated form, no matter how wild it is, can excel in rich flavor
the sauce they make. It is worth while to grow wild gooseberries,
in order to have them spiced for serving with roast fowl and game
in winter.

SMOOTH-FRUITED GOOSEBERRY, OR NORTHERN GOOSEBERRY

Ribes oxyacanthoides

Grossularia oxyacanthoides

THIS shrub grows from two to four feet high with slender, reclining branches. The spines are less numerous than and not so
long as those of the last species. The leaves are alternate, rather
deeply three- to five-lobed. The lobes are irregular or toothed. The
under surface of the leaves is soft pubescent. The flowers are
greenish purple or nearly white. The round fruits on short stems
are each about half an inch in diameter, smooth, reddish purple with
a bloom when ripe. The skin is quite thin, and the flavor is agreeable.

The Smooth Gooseberry grows in low grounds and wet woods
from Newfoundland to Manitoba and British Columbia, south to
southern New York, Michigan, and Montana. It is the parent of
Houghton, Downing, and other cultivated varieties.

I am sorry that I did not know this wild fruit when I was a boy.
I have gathered it in the northern part of New York State near
the St. Lawrence River and enjoyed eating the berries. It is excellent for the making of pies and jellies. The berries are ripe in
midsummer.

GOOSEBERRIES

OTHER species of gooseberries are found growing in this country,
but they are generally not so common or so valuable for their fruit.
Among them are the following:

Missouri, or Slender, Gooseberry (Ribes gracile, *Grossularia
missouriensis*), with a few spines and prickles, three- to five-lobed
leaves, and white flowers. The smooth, brown or purplish berries

are about half an inch in diameter. Minnesota to South Dakota, and south to Illinois, Tennessee, and Kansas.

Bristly Gooseberry (Ribes setosum, *Grossularia setosa*), with rather long spines and numerous bristles. White flowers and red to black fruit, generally with some bristles but sometimes smooth. Found in thickets and on lake shores, western Ontario to Manitoba, south to Nebraska and Wyoming.

Eastern Wild Gooseberry, or Smooth Gooseberry (Ribes rotundifolium, *Grossularia rotundifolia*), with few short spines and prickles or none, short greenish purple flowers and purple berries about one-third of an inch in diameter. Western Massachusetts, southeastern New York, south along the mountains to North Carolina.

European or Garden Gooseberry (Ribes Grossularia, *Grossularia reclinata*), with stout spines at the nodes, usually three together, and scattered prickles, and large nearly round berries, often with weak bristles, has escaped in places in New York and New Jersey.

In their Journal, Lewis and Clark record feasting in western Montana on a great variety of wild berries and purple, yellow, and black currants, which were delicious and more pleasing to the palate than those grown in their Virginia home gardens.

WILD, VIRGINIA, OR SCARLET STRAWBERRY

Fragaria virginiana

THIS well known plant is too common to need description. The leaves come from the roots and are on long stems or petioles covered with soft hairs. They are composed of three broad leaflets with saw-toothed edges. The white flowers are borne on stems shorter than those of the leaves. The red pulpy berries are ripe in June or July, according to locality and season. The seeds, or achenes as botanists call them, are imbedded in little pits on the surface. The fruit ripens in early summer.

The range of the Scarlet Strawberry is from New Brunswick to Saskatchewan and on south to Florida, Texas, and Arizona. A northern form with narrower leaflets and more oblong fruit has been described as a separate species (*Fragaria canadensis*). I find apparently no difference in the flavor of the fruit.

It was Dr. William Butler who said of strawberries, "Doubtless

God could have made a better berry, but doubtless God never did."
The wild strawberry has a delicacy of flavor all its own rarely approached by the cultivated varieties. Another naturalist, a great
lover of this wilding, wrote: "I had rather have one pint of wild
strawberries than a gallon of tame ones."

Taking these two statements into account, it would seem that
the wild strawberry is the most delicious of all our wild fruits. I
think I would agree, and I say this just after partaking of a dish
of these wild berries, gathered and prepared by my own hands, and
served with sugar and cream.

There are several other kinds of wild fruits that are close rivals,
that are found in much greater abundance and are of less trouble
to gather, but I can recall none that have such an appeal to the
eye, the sense of smell, and that of taste.

The thought of wild strawberries always leads me back to boyhood, to green fields and running brooks with bobolinks in the
meadows, bumblebees on the clover, and butterflies in air. We saw
so many things besides the strawberries we gathered to appease our
appetites or to take home for dessert.

I was recently given a small jar of wild strawberries that were
taken fresh from the field, carefully washed; some syrup was added,
and then they were cured or preserved, by some means, only in the
hot sun. The berries remained whole, but they were delicious.

EUROPEAN WOOD STRAWBERRY

Fragaria vesca

THIS plant greatly resembles the last species but is generally
more robust, and the flower stems are usually longer than the leaves.
The fruit is more conical, and as a general thing, is larger than that
of the Virginia strawberry. The seeds are not imbedded but instead, are found on the nearly smooth surface. The berries are red.
The plant is found in the eastern states in fields, along roadsides,
and in dry open woods. This plant appears to have been introduced
from Europe; but that is questionable, as there is a native variety,
somewhat smaller, that is found in open rocky woods from New
Brunswick to New Jersey and west to Oregon. A variety with
creamy white berries, sweet and delicious, is found from western
New York to West Virginia. This white-fruited form was the

strawberry that I knew best as a boy. I often gathered it by the
pint. My grandfather cultivated it in his garden seventy-five years
ago. Under cultivation, the fruit is said to be much larger than
the wild form.

The mere mention of wild strawberries takes many of us back
to the scenes of our youth and I am sorry for the boy or girl who

European Wood Strawberry (Fragaria vesca)

has never had the experience that was John Greenleaf Whittier's
as a barefoot boy:

> With thy red lip, redder still
> Kissed by strawberries on the hill.

The California Strawberry, Fragaria californica, is a western
species with small but delicious berries. A variety of the eastern
strawberry, Fragaria virginiana, also grows in California. Dr. Hall
says, "Visitors to the Yosemite are not long in locating the strawberry beds and filling their baskets with the luscious fruit."

PURPLE-FLOWERING, OR VIRGINIA, RASPBERRY

Rubus odoratus

THIS shrubby plant grows from three to five feet high. It has no prickles; but the stems are bristly, and the younger twigs are covered with sticky hairs. The large leaves, sometimes nearly a foot across, are from three- to five-lobed, with heart-shaped bases. The large, showy purple blossoms are sometimes two inches in

Purple-Flowering Raspberry (Rubus odoratus)

diameter. The fruit is a flattened red berry, ripe in July and August.

The plant is found from Nova Scotia to Georgia and west to Michigan and Tennessee. The berries are generally referred to as scarcely edible, probably because they are slightly insipid. I find they are rather pleasant, and I have seen a group of boys eat them with enjoyment. I have gone berrying with friends to "burnt lands" of northern New York where these raspberries were abundant. They were gathered along with blackcaps and red raspberries all mixed together and used for pies, jams, and jellies.

I have taken the large leaves of this species and folded the edges together, pinning them with the long spines of the hawthorn in order to make vessels to carry home wild fruits of various kinds when I came across them unexpectedly in the woods.

The Salmonberry, or White-Flowering Raspberry, also called Thimbleberry (Rubus parviflorus), is very similar to the preceding species. The blossoms are white of about the same size, and the leaves and fruit are about the same as the purple-flowering species. The stems are less bristly and clammy. It ranges from Michigan and Minnesota west to Alaska and California, and south to Colorado and Utah. It is often abundant in the far Northwest, and is much used by both Indians and whites.

WILD RED RASPBERRY

Rubus strigosus

THIS raspberry grows from two to five feet tall, is somewhat shrubby, and has numerous glandular bristles and scattered small-hooked prickles on the stem. The leaves are composed of three to five irregular, saw-toothed leaflets which are whitish, downy beneath. The flowers are white or greenish white, about half an inch across. The fruit, which is ripe from July to September, is light red, juicy, and very pleasing to the taste.

The wild red raspberry is native from Newfoundland and Labrador to Manitoba and British Columbia, and south in the Rockies to New Mexico, and in the Appalachian Mountains to North Carolina. The form in the northern part of its range is believed by some botanists to be the same as the wild red raspberry of Europe and Asia, Rubus idaeus. It varies greatly with the climate and other physical features. It is very common in open rocky places in the Catskill Mountains. I have gathered it there on sunny slopes from 2,500 to 3,700 feet altitude, where the plants were larger and the berries bigger than they are at lower elevations.

This is certainly one of our best wild fruits. I am sorry that it did not grow anywhere near my home when I was a boy. South of New York and the Great Lakes region it is apparently found in scattered patches in mountainous sections. We were, however, familiar with the cultivated forms, the Hansall, Cuthbert, and other varieties of raspberries that were derived from this species. The wild berries may be used for any purpose and in any manner that the cultivated varieties are used.

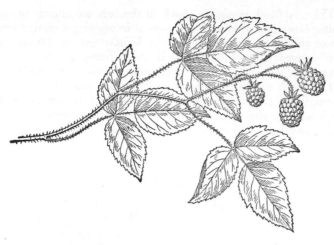

Wild Red Raspberry (Rubus strigosus)

Hither soon as spring is fled
You and Charles and I will walk;
Lurking berries, ripe and red,
Then will hang on every stalk,
Each within its leafy bower;
And for that promise spare the flower!
                    —WORDSWORTH, "Foresight"

BLACK RASPBERRY, THIMBLEBERRY, BLACKCAP
Rubus occidentalis

THE stems or canes are often six or eight feet long or more.
When the tips touch the ground they take root. The stems are
glaucous or whitened with a bloom and are armed with hooked
prickles. The leaves are composed of three (rarely five) double-
serrate leaflets which are white and downy beneath. The flowers
in size and appearance are much like those of the red raspberry.
The purple-black fruit is ripe in July and August, or as early as
June in the southern part of its range.

This plant is native from Quebec and Ontario south to Missouri
and Georgia. It is very common along fence rows, in clearings and
burnt-over lands.

The wild black raspberry stands at the very top among our wild fruits. None in my opinion surpasses it in pleasing flavor. A number of cultivated forms, such as the Kansas and the Gregg, have been derived from this species. In flavor, they are probably no better than the wild ones but are larger and more productive.

The black raspberry grows much farther south than the red species. This fruit was very valuable to the early settlers and is much sought after today. These berries are excellent for pies, jellies, and jams, and certainly nothing could be better for dessert

Black Raspberry (Rubus occidentalis)

when served with sugar and cream. Being quite firm, they are easily dried or preserved. As a boy, I gathered them by the quart from wild plants and took toll as they dropped into the pail. I can fully sympathize with Monroe Sprowl, who said:

> If ever I dies an' yo ain't certain I's dead,
> Just butter some biscuit an' new made bread
> An' spread 'em all over with raspberry jam,
> Then step mighty softly to whar I am
> An' wave dem vittles above my head,—
> If my mouf don't open, I'm certainly dead.

The Purple Raspberry, Rubus neglectus, found in rocky woods from New England to Pennsylvania and west to Ontario and Ohio, is probably a self-perpetuating hybrid as it is intermediate between the red and the black species. The berries are a little more tart than either of the two. It is the parent of several cultivated

varieties. Perhaps this is the species that Emerson had in mind
when he wrote:

> The purple berries in the wood
> Supplied me necessary food.

The Wild Raspberry of the far western states, Rubus leucoder-
mis, is also an excellent wild species. The fruit is either black or
red. Dr. Harvey M. Hall says, "Its berries are as highly flavored
as those of any cultivated species and are eagerly sought by campers,
who usually find, however, that the birds have preceded them."

THE DWARF RASPBERRY
Rubus triflorus
Rubus americanus

THIS berry is found in swamps and wet woods from Labrador
to Alaska and south to New Jersey, Ohio, and Nebraska. The
reddish purple fruit is quite large and juicy. Some authors state
that the berries are sour, but my experience is that, when fully ripe,
they are rather sweet and very pleasant. The only trouble is that
very few berries form and the plant itself is rare in many parts of
its range.

The Dwarf Raspberry is apparently intermediate between the
blackberries and raspberries. The plant is low, generally trailing,
herbaceous or only slightly woody, with three (rarely five) leaflets
and no prickles. The fruit is ripe in July and August.

CLOUDBERRY, OR BAKED-APPLE BERRY
Rubus Chamaemorus

AN interesting little raspberry is found from the mountains of
Maine and New Hampshire north to arctic America and west to
British Columbia and Alaska. It grows in bogs and moist places
and reaches a height of four to ten inches, from a creeping herbaceous rootstock. The leaves, two or three in number, are nearly
round, slightly five-lobed. The solitary white flower is followed by
an amber-colored fruit which is juicy and pleasant when ripe. It
is gathered and sold in the markets of cities and towns of Nova
Scotia and Newfoundland, and travelers who have seen and eaten

them there are often curious to know more about the Baked-Apple Berry.

MOUNTAIN, OR HIGH-BUSH, BLACKBERRY

Rubus allegheniensis

Rubus nigrobaccus

THIS is a rather robust plant, growing from three to seven feet high, erect or arching. The older stems are reddish or purplish and very prickly. The leaflets are in fives or threes, and are soft

Mountain Blackberry (Rubus allegheniensis)

and hairy beneath. The flower cluster is glandular hairy. The white flowers, in terminal and axillary racemes, are from an inch to an inch and a half in diameter. The berries are oblong or conic, generally more than twice as long as they are wide, and are composed of numerous, rather small drupelets. The slender berries are more solid and less juicy than those of most other species. This plant is found from Nova Scotia and Ontario south to North Carolina, Virginia, and Illinois.

The species of blackberries are numerous and difficult to separate botanically; thus much confusion seems to exist in botanical literature concerning them. For our purpose we will include the High-Bush Blackberries in two species.

The Mountain Blackberry is not confined to mountainous regions alone but is more abundant in such localities. It may be told by the long, compact fruit and the red stems of the leaves and fruit clusters. The berries have a peculiar pleasant flavor, sometimes slightly spicy. The fruit is usually ripe in July and August.

TALL, OR HIGH-BUSH, BLACKBERRY, OR THIMBLEBERRY

Rubus villosus

Rubus argutus

THIS plant grows erect or curved, branched and shrubby, from three to nine feet high, armed with strong recurved prickles. The leaves are composed of three ovate leaflets, the end one stalked. They are soft and downy beneath. The flower clusters are in broad racemes, chiefly at the ends of the branches. The white flowers are about an inch across. The black fruits are from half an inch to an inch long, often nearly as wide. The drupelets composing the berries are rather large and juicy. This plant ranges from New England to Michigan, south to Florida and Arkansas. Several species are included in the range too difficult for the beginner to separate.

The fruit of the High-Bush Blackberry varies wonderfully. Some are large, some small; some are sweet, others sour. Occasionally we come across plants that are very productive, while others produce but few fruits. The High-Bush Blackberry grows in old fields, along fence rows and roadsides, and in open woods and thickets. The blackberry is probably our most valuable wild fruit. It grows in some form over almost the entire eastern United States, and the annual crop is worth millions to the inhabitants. Several splendid cultivated forms such as the Lawton and the Kittatinny have been derived from the wild species.

The mere mention of blackberries will bring to the minds of many who have had contact with the country, the various excursions they have made for this wild fruit. Going berrying was a favorite youthful pastime of the writer. In fact, I cannot remember when I was too young to go berrying, for as Emerson says, I was often

> Caught among the blackberry vines,
> Feeding on the Ethiops sweet.

Berrying had so many pleasant surprises, and we came in contact with and saw so much of wild nature, of plant and animal, bird and insect life, that we were always ready to repeat the experience. When this wild fruit was at its best, we did not ask for sweeter things.

> For my taste the blackberry cone
> Purpled over hedge and stone.
> —WHITTIER

DEWBERRY, OR CREEPING OR RUNNING BLACKBERRY

Rubus procumbens

Rubus canadensis

CHARACTERISTICS: Stems trailing often several feet long, slightly woody, armed with scattered stout prickles. Branches ascending, four to twelve inches long; leaflets three to seven. White flowers about an inch across. Black fruits, often nearly an inch long and about as broad, composed of large juicy drupelets.

The Dewberry when ripe is of excellent flavor and of large size, but the plants are generally not so productive as those of the blackberry.

The Dewberry ranges from Maine to western Ontario, and south to Virginia, Louisiana, and Oklahoma.

The Southern Dewberry, Rubus trivialis, a very similar species found from Virginia to Florida and Texas, chiefly near the coast, is probably the most important berry of that region.

The Dewberry grows in dry, gravelly or stony soil, in fields, along roadways, and on rocky hillsides. Farmers often despise it because it overruns their wheat and oat fields.

Walt Whitman saw beauty in the vine when he wrote:

The running blackberry would adorn the parlors of heaven.

Dewberry (Rubus procumbens)

Yes, Whitman saw more than beauty in this plant for elsewhere
he notes

That blackberries are so flavorous and juicy.

PEAR, OR CHOKE PEAR
Pyrus communis

THE Pear, a native of Europe and Asia, has escaped from cultivation from Maine to New York, New Jersey, and Pennsylvania.
Sometimes these wild trees are two feet or more in diameter and
fifty feet in height. The branches are generally rough and thorny,
the leaves finely toothed or entire, with a pointed apex and a
rounded base. The white flowers are an inch or more across. The
fruit of the wild tree has the usual pear shape but is seldom more
than two inches long. The tree is found in thickets, and along fence
rows, or sometimes in old neglected orchards.

The fruit of the Choke Pear is generally not agreeable to the taste in the raw state; but I have known housewives to make excellent preserves from it, and the hard, solid flesh makes it desirable for pickled pears. Occasionally we come across a tree with edible fruits, and I have known boys to fill their pockets and hats with

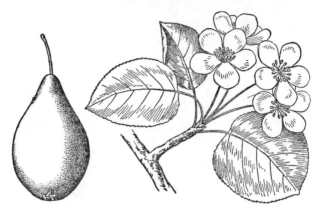

Choke Pear (Pyrus communis)

them to take home or to eat at their leisure. The fruit is ripe or fit for use in August and September.

NARROW-LEAVED CRAB APPLE, OR WILD CRAB APPLE TREE

Pyrus angustifolia

THE Narrow-Leaved Crab Apple grows generally not more than twenty or twenty-five feet high. The twigs often end in spines or thorns. The oblong, rather narrow leaves are glossy above with slightly toothed or nearly entire margins. Those of young shoots are often slightly lobed. The pink, fragrant blossoms are about an inch across. The greenish yellow fruits, about an inch in diameter, usually fall with the leaves; but sometimes they cling to the naked branches even after they are frozen. They are hard and sour but are often used for preserves and pickles.

The Narrow-Leaved Crab Apple is found in woods and thickets from New Jersey to Illinois and Kansas, south to Florida and Louisiana. The apples are gathered in late autumn, and besides the uses mentioned above, they are in demand for jelly.

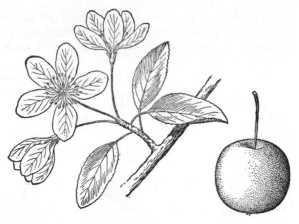

Narrow-Leaved Crab Apple (Pyrus angustifolia)

AMERICAN CRAB APPLE

Pyrus coronaria

Malus glaucescens

THE American Crab Apple tree sometimes attains a height of twenty-five feet and a trunk diameter of ten inches, the branchlets somewhat armed with spines. The ovate leaves are sharply saw-

American Crab Apple (Pyrus coronaria)

toothed, sometimes lobed and with rounded or slightly heart-shaped bases. The rose-colored blossoms are from an inch to two inches across and are among the most sweetly scented of all our wild flowers. The yellow-green fruits are similar to those of the preceding species but are larger, often reaching a diameter of an inch and a half.

The American Crab Apple is found in woods, thickets, and along roadsides from Ontario and Michigan south to New Jersey, South Carolina, and west to Iowa and Missouri. The apples are hard and sour, but they have a pleasing odor and may be kept for weeks. They cannot be eaten raw but are excellent for preserves and pickles, and few wild fruits make better jelly. They should be gathered in late autumn when the leaves have fallen.

The early settlers collected the crab apples in autumn and buried them. By spring the apples had lost much of their acid and were then made into cider, jelly, or preserves. The custom of burying the apples was probably derived from the Indians, who made much use of this wild fruit.

At a few places in southwestern Pennsylvania I have seen almost impenetrable thickets of wild crab apples, each several acres in extent. At blossom time in May they present a sea of pink, filling the air with a delightful odor. In October, 1938, I went by a small thicket where the ground was fairly covered with wild crab apples.

The Western Crab Apple, Pyrus ioensis, *Malus ioensis,* is quite similar to the American Crab Apple. The leaves are oval or oblong and woolly beneath, especially when young. It is found from Wisconsin and Minnesota south to Louisiana and Oklahoma. It has horticultural possibilities.

The well known Siberian Crab Apple, Pyrus baccata, with its red or yellowish fruit is escaping from cultivation in New England.

The common apple of cultivation has hybridized with some of the wild species, making puzzling forms. These exist in some parts of the United States.

OREGON CRAB APPLE

Pyrus diversifolia

Pyrus rivularis

THE Oregon Crab Apple ranges from Alaska to California. The tree reaches a height of thirty feet, or sometimes is only a shrub. The leaves are ovate, occasionally three-lobed, pointed with sawtoothed edges, paler beneath, later changing to brownish on the underside. The blossoms are white and are followed by a small apple which is slightly oblong, scarcely more than half an inch in diameter. The fruit is first yellowish, gradually changing to purple.

This is the only species of wild crab apple on the Pacific Coast. The white settlers used the fruit in early times for jelly, and it is yet used for that purpose. It was also eaten by the Indians.

THE APPLE OR WILDING TREE

Pyrus Malus

Malus Malus

THE common or cultivated Apple, a native of Europe and Asia, has escaped to roadsides, fence rows, woods, and thickets from New England to Virginia and Ohio. In April or May, its presence is detected by masses of pink or white fragrant blossoms. These apples are of various sizes, shapes, and colors; or, as Christina Rossetti has poetically expressed it,

> Some glow golden in the sun,
> Some show green and streaked,
> Some set forth a purple bloom,
> Some blush rosy-cheeked.

Plant the seeds of an apple and you rarely get anything like the variety that you planted. The majority of them are of little value as apples. Of the dozens of wild trees whose fruit I have tested, I know of at least two that were worthy of being named and cultivated.

It is said that some of our best cultivated varieties originated in this way. The last time that I went by the country school which I attended as a boy, I was impressed by the number of wild Apple trees that grew along the old rail fence that enclosed the grounds. Others were growing in the waste lands beyond. Some of these trees were bearing fruit. Apples were a part of the daily lunch of nearly every country schoolboy in southwestern Pennsylvania where I spent my youth.

The uncultivated apple, like the majority of our wild fruits, is most enjoyed when we are tramping through field and woodland, especially when we are tired and hungry. Henry D. Thoreau in his excellent essay on "Wild Apples" says:

To appreciate the wild and sharp flavors of these October fruits, it is necessary that you be breathing the sharp October or November air. The outdoor air and exercise which the walker gets, give a different tone to his palate, and he craves a fruit which the sedentary would call harsh and crabbed. They must be eaten in the fields, when your system is all aglow with exercise, when the frosty weather nips your fingers, the wind rattles the bare boughs or rustles the few remaining leaves, and the jay is heard screaming around. What is sour in the house, a bracing walk makes sweet. Some of these apples might be labeled, "To be eaten in the wind."

The Apple was introduced into Massachusetts as early as 1629, and was very important to the colonists and pioneers. Nearly all the early orchards were of seedling trees, and occasionally from among these seedlings an excellent apple was developed. The Baldwin came from Massachusetts; the Wealthy, from Minnesota; the Northern Spy, from New York State. A good example is the McIntosh Red. John McIntosh, a pioneer, settled at what is now Dundela, Ontario. In 1796, while clearing a forest, he came across some small seedling apple trees. These he planted near his house. One of the trees bore extra-fine apples, and it was given the name of McIntosh Red. This tree lived and bore fruit for one hundred and twelve years, dying in 1908 after being injured by a fire. By popular subscription a monument was later erected to mark the site of the original tree of one of our finest American apples.

Wild or seedling apples can be used for practically all the purposes that the better cultivated varieties are put to although we prefer the latter. Apple sauce, pies, fritters, and dumplings have always been appreciated by the American people. Dried apples were much used in pioneer days, as they helped to bridge out the season and could be transported long distances when traveling. When apples are not good enough for other purposes, they are made into cider which is allowed to change to vinegar. There was a time when apple butter was considered a necessary article in almost every rural household. A barrel of cider was boiled in a large kettle until there was only about one-third of the original volume. Apples to the extent of half a barrel, or more (sweet ones preferred), were carefully pared, cut into quarters or eighths, and the cores removed. These were put into the cider and boiling continued slowly, the mass being stirred all the while with a long-handled wooden "stir stick" or ladle until a sauce or butter of the right consistency was formed. Usually no sugar was added. The result was a dozen gallons, more or less, of apple butter that could be kept all through the year.

Of course we are all familiar with the work of John Chapman, better known as Johnny Appleseed, the horticultural missionary, who went ahead of the white settlers and planted apple seeds in many places over Ohio and Indiana. The author's great-grandfather crossed the Appalachian Mountains and settled in southwestern Pennsylvania before 1800. That region then was scarcely more than an Indian wilderness. He planted an orchard and erected a cider mill, better known as a cider press, one of the first in that part of the country. When I was a small boy, long before I saw the name of Johnny Appleseed in print, I was thrilled by the story told by my grandfather how Johnny came to my great-grandfather's cider press, washed the seeds out of the discarded pomace, and dried them. After he had obtained a sufficient quantity of seeds, he placed them in a bag and marched off to the Ohio wilderness, avoiding the Indians or making peace with them, and planting the seeds in open places or where he thought they would grow best. He had the true missionary spirit.

JUNEBERRY, OR SERVICEBERRY, OR SHADBUSH
Amelanchier canadensis

THE Juneberry, or Serviceberry, grows to be a tree sometimes a foot in diameter and fifty feet high, but it is usually much smaller. The light-colored bark is smooth or, on larger trees, slightly streaked or nettled near the base. The alternate leaves are oval and somewhat pointed, rounded at the base with fine saw-toothed edges. The white flowers sometimes appear in March in the South, but in April or early May farther north. They are arranged in the form of loose racemes. The tree when in bloom in the spring may be seen for a mile. The round berries are a quarter of an inch or more in diameter, red or purplish, and of a sweet and pleasant odor.

This tree has a wide range, being found from Nova Scotia to western Ontario, south to Florida and Louisiana. It is most abundant in dry soil and is very common on river banks and hillsides, and blooms just about the time that the shad run up the streams— hence the name Shadbush.

The wood is very hard, tough, and elastic. Any tree that is not too large may be bent to the ground without breaking, so that the berries can be gathered from the branches; when released, it will spring back into the natural position. The berries may be served uncooked for dessert. They are excellent for pies and for canning for winter use.

I have made much use of serviceberries when camping in the woods, sometimes gathering quarts of them. They ripen in June or early July. The largest and best that I have ever seen were in the southern Catskill Mountains at an elevation of 2,000 to 2,500 feet; some of these were half an inch in diameter and of excellent flavor. I have found them nearly as large in the mountains of central Pennsylvania.

On a mountain top in Maine, I once unexpectedly came across serviceberries on bushes not more than two feet high. They were

Juneberry (Amelanchier canadensis)

large and abundant, and the leaves and fruit were just like those on the trees farther south. The berries were of excellent flavor and were much appreciated by a hungry tramper. This was in the month of August.

NORTHWESTERN JUNEBERRY, OR SERVICEBERRY
Amelanchier alnifolia

THIS is a common shrub of the Northwest, ranging from western Ontario to British Columbia, south to Nebraska, Colorado, and California. It grows from six to eight feet tall. The leaves vary from elliptical to nearly round. They are blunt at the apex, rounded at the base, and toothed above the middle. The flowers are white in short racemes. The berries, when fully ripe, are dark purple with a bloom. They are sweet and edible. The plant is often cultivated for its fruit in the East.

This shrub provides an important article of food among the Indians of the Northwest, who gather the berries in large numbers and often dry them for future use. Dr. Harvey M. Hall, speaking of the shrub in California says, "The edible pulp is an article of food among the Indians, but its sickly-sweetish taste is not pleasant to epicurean palates."

Lewis and Clark speak of the fine quality of the wild fruit and the use the Indians made of it. They often crushed the berries and dried them, forming a kind of cake that could be carried on their journeys. Pieces could be broken off from the mass to cook with meat or vegetable food. It was also used for pemmican—dried meat, pounded fine, mixed with dried fruit and animal fat; the mass molded in the form of cakes.

There are other species of Serviceberry in the eastern United States. One, the Swamp Sugar Pear, or Currant Tree, Amelanchier intermedia, is sometimes cultivated. It is found in swampy or moist soil. Its sweet berries are dark purple with a bloom. The birds are very fond of them, as they are of all our other serviceberries.

Another species, the Oblong-Fruited Juneberry, Amelanchier Bartramiana, is a shrub that grows three to nine feet high in swampy places. The berries are oval or pear-shaped, purple with a bloom. The plant does not grow south of Pennsylvania, but I have gathered and eaten it with relish in the northern part of New York State.

In *Flora of New Mexico,* Wooton and Standley catalogue eight species of serviceberries native of that state. They give the following note, "The fruits of the native serviceberries were a favorite food among the Indians in earlier days. They were eaten fresh or were dried and preserved for winter use. They are insipid in all the species. Those of the species which grow at lower levels are nearly dry and consequently useless for food."

HAWTHORN, OR RED HAW, OR THORN APPLE
Crataegus

THE fruits of twenty species of hawthorns have been recorded as edible. As the identification of the various species of hawthorns is generally left to specialists, with much disagreement among themselves, I shall not attempt to describe the edible species of this difficult genus.

The hawthorns, which are close relatives of the apples, comprise shrubs or small trees with simple, usually lobed leaves and characteristic sharp-pointed thorns or spines an inch to five inches long. The white flowers are in terminal clusters. The fruit, generally red, sometimes yellow, resembles tiny apples. The hard seeds are surrounded by a dry or pulpy flesh which is edible in some species but not palatable in a large majority of them. This flesh may be used for jelly.

Hawthorns are very common from the eastern United States west to the plains. They are especially abundant in limestone areas along the borders of the Appalachian Mountains. Only occasionally do we find a tree with edible fruits. One stood by a fence between pasture fields near my old home in southwestern Pennsylvania. This hawthorn was treelike, with smooth gray or light-colored bark and numerous stiff-pointed spines two or three inches long. The bright red fruits became ripe in September or early October, and were slightly oval, three-quarters of an inch to an inch long, somewhat juicy, meaty, and pleasing to the taste. Insect larvae rarely attacked them. The fruits of this hawthorn were the best in all the countryside—the best red haws that I have ever known. As boys, we often filled our pockets with them to eat at our leisure. The tree in most respects corresponded to the botanical description of Crataegus mollis and was probably of this species or a closely related one.

The May Haw of the southern states, Crataegus aestivalis, has rather large fruits for a hawthorn. They ripen in May and June and are frequently made into preserves and jellies. In September, 1933, I saw people in the mountains east of Salt Lake City, Utah, gathering large quantities of the fruits of the Western Black Hawthorn, Crataegus rivularis, for jams and jellies.

I am informed that the hips or fruits of the California Wild Rose, Rosa californica, which is common, often abundant, in California and southern Oregon, are sometimes used for jelly.

WILD PLUM, OR YELLOW OR RED PLUM
Prunus americana

THE Wild Plum grows to be a small tree, but sometimes is only a shrub with numerous branches somewhat thorny and with rather thick rough bark. The ovate or oblong leaves, round at the base, have long tapering points and are sharply, often doubly, saw-toothed. In April or early May, the tree is covered with masses of white flowers followed by round red, sometimes yellow fruits, which are ripe in August or September. The plums are nearly an inch in diameter, pulpy, with a rather tough skin. When fully ripe, they are very pleasing to eat. Many cultivated varieties have been developed from the wild plum. This tree ranges from Connecticut to Montana, south to Florida, Texas, and Colorado. In the Missis-

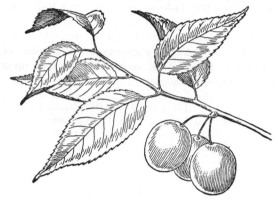

Wild Plum (Prunus americana)

sippi valley the fruit is larger and better, and it is from this region that the cultivated varieties were developed.

The American wild plum is excellent for preserves and jellies and is often in great demand. I have seen pecks of the fruit in the country markets of Pennsylvania. Part of August and September, 1934, I spent in New Mexico, where I found the trees growing about the Indian villages in the northern part of the state. The rather large size and the abundance of the fruit would indicate that the trees may have been selected and planted. Those growing in out-of-the-way places and in thickets were native or had escaped. Some of the dried fruits were secured from the Indians. They were palatable when stewed, with enough sugar added.

George Catlin, the artist, writing of his travels about 1837 among the Indians in the region of Oklahoma, speaks of the abundance of wild plums as follows:

The next hour we would be trailing through broad and verdant valleys of green prairies, into which we had descended; and oftentimes find our progress completely arrested by hundreds of acres of small plum trees of four to six feet in height; so closely interwoven and interlocked together, as entirely to dispute our progress, and sending us several miles around; when every bush that was in sight was so loaded with the weight of its delicious wild fruit, that they were in many instances literally without leaves on their branches and bent quite to the ground.

Not every wild plum tree bears abundance of fruit; many of them seem to be self-sterile. Trees often stand year after year with scarcely any fruit at all. When a tree does bear well, the boy who knows it has a treat in store for himself. In my boyhood days, we often took long rambles in search of wild plums, and when we found real good ones we enjoyed them almost as much as James Whitcomb Riley, the Hoosier poet, who tells of his boyhood that, up and down old Brandywine Creek, they got

> Jes' *gorges* o' wild plums,
> Till a feller'd suck his thumbs
> Clean up to his elbows! *My!—*
> *Me some more er lem me die!* [1]

CANADA PLUM, OR HORSE PLUM
Prunus nigra

THE Canada Plum is a species very similar to the Wild Plum just described but is more northern in its distribution, extending from Newfoundland to Alberta, south to southern New England and Wisconsin. It is most abundant along the Great Lakes and in the St. Lawrence valley.

The branches of this small tree are stiff, armed with blunt spines. The petioles generally have two red glands near the leaf blade. The leaves are broadly obovate with usually gland-tipped saw teeth. The apex is long-pointed. The flowers are white but sometimes turn pink just before the petals fall. They are larger than those of the American Wild Plum. The fruits are from an inch to an inch and a third long, oval, reddish or yellowish blotched with red, with a thick skin and pulpy flesh that clings to the seed. They are gathered in large quantities and sold in the markets of southern Canada and the northern United States. They are generally made

---

[1] From "Armazindy" by James Whitcomb Riley, copyright 1894, 1922. Used by special permission of the publishers, The Bobbs-Merrill Company.

into jellies and preserves but are often stewed or eaten raw. They ripen in August and September.

This plum is most common along streams and in thickets but is frequently met with along roadsides. Some botanists consider it only a variety of the American Wild Plum, with which it hybridizes or intergrades. I first saw it in the St. Lawrence valley, where I

Canada Plum (Prunus nigra)

gathered and enjoyed the fruits. I recognized it at once as being different from the more southern species. Some excellent cultivated varieties have been developed from the Canada Plum.

WILD GOOSE PLUM

Prunus hortulana

Prunus Munsoniana

THE Wild Goose Plum is a native of the Mississippi valley from West Virginia to Kansas, south to Mississippi and Texas. It is generally regarded as a natural hybrid between the Chickasaw Plum and the American Wild Plum. It forms a small, round-topped tree, sometimes reaching a height of twenty-five feet. with a trunk nearly a foot in diameter. The rigid branches are without spines. The reddish brown twigs bear oblong or ovate taper-pointed leaves. The flowers appear with the leaves. The fruit, which ripens from August to early October, is nearly round, about an inch long, bright red or yellowish red, juicy, and of an agreeable flavor. The flesh is inclined to cling to the stone. This tree is the parent of many cultivated varieties, among them being the Miner and the Wayland.

The Wild Goose Plum in its native state is said to be quite a rare tree, growing chiefly in lowlands along streams, but I have never seen it. I am familiar with the cultivated forms, which sometimes escape to roadsides and waste lands.

The common name of this species is interesting. It is claimed that a man in Tennessee shot a wild goose and found a plum seed in its crop. This seed, when planted, produced one of the first known trees of this species. Another version of the origin of the common name is that a man near Columbia, Tennessee, shot a wild goose: at the spot where the carcass was thrown down, this plum came up the following spring.

SIERRA, PACIFIC, OR CALIFORNIA PLUM
Prunus subcordata

THE Sierra Plum forms a bush or very small tree from three to fifteen feet high, and is found in the northern half of California and in the southern part of Oregon. The thick leaves are ovate or nearly round. The white flowers grow two to four in a cluster. The dark red fruit is nearly round. The slightly acid flesh clings to the stone. This plum varies much with the locality. In the southern part of its range, it is apt to be small, dry, and unpalatable. Farther north, it grows much larger and is gathered in large quantities and eaten fresh or made into delicious preserves.

BEACH PLUM
Prunus maritima

THE Beach Plum is a low-branching shrub from two to six feet high, without thorns. The oval leaves have sharp saw-tooth edges. The numerous white showy flowers appear before the leaves. The round, dull purple fruits, which are ripe in August and September, are covered with a dense bloom. They are from half an inch to an inch in diameter. The skin is quite thick and tough, but when fully ripe the pulp is sweet and juicy, free from the stone. I have enjoyed eating them.

The Beach Plum is native from New Brunswick to Virginia, on sea beaches and sand dunes. Sometimes it may be found on dry sandy hills twenty miles inland. At some places along the New

Beach Plum (Prunus maritima)

England coast, the plums are gathered in large quantities and sold in the local markets for preserving. They are excellent for jelly.

CHICKASAW PLUM, OR MOUNTAIN CHERRY

Prunus angustifolia

THIS is a small tree, rarely twenty feet high, with branches somewhat thorny. The leaves are narrow or oblong lanceolate with fine saw-tooth edges. The flowers expand before the leaves. The fruit, which ripens in June and July, is bright red, nearly round and from a half to three-fourths of an inch in diameter. The skin is thin, and the pulp soft and sweet. The fruit from wild trees is gathered and sold in the markets of the South. It is said to be unexcelled for jellies and preserves.

The Chickasaw Plum is native from Delaware to Florida and west to Kansas and Texas. In places it forms dense thickets. It is the parent of a dozen cultivated varieties.

The Sand Plum of Nebraska and Kansas, Prunus Watsoni, is probably only a variety of the Chickasaw. It is a bush three or four feet high, growing on the sand hills of those states. We find recorded that the early settlers gathered its fruits by the bushels for pies, preserves, and jellies. They are still much used and appreciated.

Chickasaw Plum (Prunus angustifolia)

Porter's Plum, or Allegheny Sloe, Prunus alleghaniensis, is a spreading shrub rarely more than eight feet high. It is found from Connecticut to the mountains of Pennsylvania. The ripe fruits are purplish black with a bloom, scarcely more than half an inch long, pleasantly acid. I have gathered and eaten them in the mountains of central Pennsylvania and found them very agreeable. In that region they are much used by the natives for jams, jellies, and pies.

SWEET CHERRY, OR MAZZARD

Prunus avium

IN places from New England west to Ohio and Kentucky, the cultivated Sweet Cherry, a native of Europe, has escaped to waste

lands, thickets, and fence rows. Occasionally it is found in deep
woods. The tree much resembles the Black Birch. The cherries
are either black or red and are often as large and palatable as those
grown in the orchards. In southwestern Pennsylvania, where I
spent my boyhood days, these were very common along roadsides,
fences, and in waste lands. I gathered large pailfuls without going

Sweet Cherry (Prunus avium)

off my father's farm. In that region, the black-fruited varieties are
called Blackhearts, and the trees that bear red fruits are termed
Redhearts. Birds usually get their full quota.

    A few years ago, one of these trees stood on the border of our
lawn. It was two feet in diameter and at least fifty feet high, and
had served as a landmark for the children of the neighborhood
many years before we first enjoyed its shade. The fruits on it were

dark brown, rather small, and slightly bitter, but the neighborhood children seemed to enjoy them. They were not pleasing to my palate. We found by experiment that they made superior jelly—equal to, if not better than, that made from the Early Richmond on the opposite side of the lawn.

The Sour Cherry, Prunus Cerasus, introduced from Europe, has also escaped from cultivation from New England to Georgia and farther west. The fruit is red or dark brown and sour. The tree is smaller and of a rounder head than that of the sweet cherry. It is always in demand for pies and jellies. Nearly all the cultivated cherries—that is, those cultivated for their edible fruits—have been developed from this and the species described above.

BLACK WILD CHERRY, OR RUM CHERRY
Prunus serotina

THIS is a large tree whose wood is much prized for lumber. The bark on trunks of older trees is dark and rough; that of the branches, smooth and reddish brown. The oblong lance-shaped leaves, with saw-tooth edges are quite thick and shining. The numerous white flowers in long racemes appear when the leaves are about half-grown. The fruit, which is ripe in August and September, is round or slightly flattened, from a third- to a half-inch in diameter, shiny black or dark purple. The juicy flesh is of a pleasant vinous flavor, slightly bitter.

This tree is native from Nova Scotia to Dakota, south to Florida and Texas. It grows in woods and open spaces, and is especially common along old fences where the seeds have been scattered by the birds. It produces more and generally better fruit when growing in fields or open spaces that admit of much sunlight. In years gone by, the fruits were much esteemed for flavoring rum and whisky, making what is known as "cherry bounce."

In my boyhood days, we gathered many of these cherries for eating raw and pronounced them good, and sometimes we induced our mothers to make pies of them. They vary wonderfully in size and quality. I once found a small tree in New York State—scarcely more than a bush—that had fruits almost as large as those of the cultivated cherry, sweet and pleasant with scarcely a taste of bitterness.

Black Wild Cherry (Prunus serotina)

CHOKE CHERRY
Prunus virginiana

THIS is a shrub or small tree rarely more than twenty feet high.
The oval leaves are from two to four inches long and about half
as wide, abruptly pointed, and with saw-tooth edges. The white
flowers, in racemes, appear when the leaves are about full-grown.
The dark red fruits, the size of peas, ripen in July and August.
Often the branches bend with their load of fruit, but the cherries are
so astringent as to pucker the mouth and affect the throat. They
are well named—Choke Cherries. Better or improved varieties of

them are cultivated in the St. Lawrence valley of Quebec. It is also recorded that in the early days, in some places, the Indians made much use of them. The astringent quality is said to disappear when cooked. In some parts of this country, they are used for jelly. Birds are very fond of these fruits.

According to Professor Sargent, this is the most widely distributed tree in North America, extending from the Arctic Circle to the southern states and Mexico and from the Atlantic to the Pacific.

Choke Cherry (Prunus virginiana)

In northern Minnesota I found Choke Cherries that were glossy black, but they had the same astringent taste as the dark red variety. They are used to some extent there for jelly. I have carried out some experiments with the Choke Cherry and it makes a fair quality of jelly; but when mixed with apple or Crab Apple the jelly is excellent. The fruit lacks pectin.

The Bird Cherry, or Pin Cherry, Prunus pennsylvanica, is found in many places in the northern part of the country. The bright red cherries are too sour for human food uncooked, but the birds are especially fond of them and soon strip the trees.

The finest specimens of the Pin Cherry that I have ever seen, I found in northern Minnesota in the autumn of 1937. On one tree, the cherries were unusually large for this species and the seeds could easily be discerned through the flesh. They were used in that region for jelly which it was claimed was good. The pin cherry should be considered when looking for jelly making material.

The Sand or Dwarf Cherry, Prunus pumila—a low bush growing in sandy places from New Brunswick to New Jersey and about the Great Lakes—and the similar shrub, the Western Sand Cherry, *Prunus Besseyi,* which is found on the plains and extends into the Rocky Mountains, have merit as wild fruits but vary greatly as to size and quality.

ROCKY MOUNTAIN CHERRY
Prunus melanocarpa

THIS small tree was once considered a variety of the common Choke Cherry, but it seems to be specifically distinct. It is found in the Rocky Mountains from Canada to New Mexico. The fruit when ripe is usually larger than that of the eastern Choke Cherry, almost black and very little astringent. I saw it growing in central Utah, where it was much used for jams and jellies. In northern New Mexico, I recently secured some of the dried fruit from the Indians; and when enough sugar was added it became quite palatable. The Indians make much use of this fruit, especially in regions where berries are scarce.

INDIAN CHERRY, OR CAROLINA BUCKTHORN
Rhamnus caroliniana

THIS is a tall thornless shrub, or sometimes a low tree. The alternate, oblong leaves are quite large with margins nearly entire. The small greenish flowers are sometimes solitary but generally clustered in the axils of the leaves. The round, three-seeded fruits are about one-third of an inch in diameter. They are crimson at first but become black when fully ripe, and are then sweet and edible.

The Indian Cherry is a member of the buckthorn family and is found in low grounds and swampy places from New Jersey, Kentucky, Missouri, and Kansas south to Florida and Texas.

The fruits of our northern buckthorns are disagreeable and astringent. The Common Buckthorn of Europe, Rhamnus cathartica, is much used for hedges in New England and the middle states and has escaped from cultivation. Its berries are not edible, but they yield a dye known as "Chinese Green." The Alder Buckthorn,

Indian Cherry (Rhamnus caroliniana)

Rhamnus Frangula, also a native of Europe, is used for "making the best charcoal for the finest gunpowder." It has been introduced in a few swampy places about New York. Its fruit is disagreeable.

The name Southern or Carolina Buckthorn is also applied to a shrub or small tree Bumelia lycioides belonging to an entirely different family. There are several species of Bumelia in Florida and along the Gulf Coast whose fruits are edible.

THE REDBERRY

Rhamnus crocea

This is another buckthorn, native of California. It varies greatly in size and appearance, sometimes being only a shrub two or three feet tall, but some varieties develop into a small tree. The small oval or elliptic leaves are stiff and evergreen. The bright red ovoid berries vary greatly in size, but usually are about one-fourth inch in diameter, pulpy, and edible.

DARLING PLUM, OR RED IRONWOOD
Reynosia latifolia

ANOTHER shrub or small tree belonging to the buckthorn family is known as the Darling Plum. It is found in Florida near the coast and on the keys, also in the Bahamas and West Indies. It is an evergreen species, with firm oblong leathery leaves and reddish brown bark, hard and scaly. The very small yellowish green flowers are arranged in axillary clusters. The one-seeded fruit or drupe is slightly oval, about three-fourths of an inch long, black, sweet, and edible. This small tree, it is said, is sometimes cultivated for its edible fruits, which are occasionally found in the public markets.

PURPLE HAW, OR BLUEWOOD
Condalia obovata

ANOTHER member of the same family is the Purple Haw of Texas and northern Mexico. It is a spiny shrub or small tree with a maximum height of twenty-five or thirty feet. The rather small leathery leaves are broadest above the middle. The nearly round fruit is a little more than one-fourth of an inch in diameter, black, sweet, and edible.

NORTHERN FOX GRAPE, OR PLUM GRAPE
Vitis labrusca

THE well known Northern Fox Grape is most at home in thickets and along borders of woods, generally trailing over bushes or on the ground but sometimes climbing tall trees. The large leaves are opposite a forked tendril or fruit cluster. They are either entire or deeply lobed, slightly toothed and rusty, woolly beneath. The fruit clusters are not large, the brownish purple berries are round and from one-half to three-fourths of an inch in diameter or even larger. They have a tough skin and a musky odor and taste. They are ripe in September or October.

This vine ranges from New England to Minnesota and south to Georgia and Tennessee.

The Concord, Catawba, Isabella, and other cultivated grapes were derived from this wild species. Its fruit is not as good as those of the cultivated forms, yet when thoroughly ripe the taste is

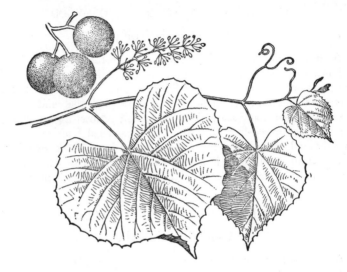

Northern Fox Grape (Vitis labrusca)

pleasant; and probably no grape is superior for jelly. The greenish flowers of this and other grapes are very fragrant, giving us one of the most pleasing wildwood odors found in nature. It may have been the blossoms of the grape but probably was the fruit that caused Helen Hunt Jackson to write:

From dewy lanes at morning
The grapes' sweet odors rise.[1]

In 1679, Jasper Dankers and Peter Sluyter left Holland for a journey to the new world. They record that on October 6th they left New York to travel on foot over Manhattan Island. New York then occupied only the extreme southern part of the Island. They

[1] "September" from "Sonnets and Lyrics" by Helen Hunt Jackson. published by Little, Brown and Company.

went north toward Harlem, leaving the village of the Bouerie on the right. Dankers wrote, "We found blue grapes along the road which were very good and sweet, and as good as any I have tasted in the Fatherland." These were likely the fox grape, but possibly one of the smaller wild grapes. The European grape failed to grow in eastern United States. In the peach orchards on Manhattan Island he saw fruit so abundant as to nearly cover the ground. It must have been wild or cultivated fruit that scented the air when he wrote, October 7, 1679: "I must add, in passing through this island we sometimes encountered such a sweet smell in the air that we stood still, because we did not know what it was we were meeting."

SUMMER GRAPE, OR PIGEON GRAPE, OR SMALL OR WILD GRAPE

Vitis aestivalis

THIS vine grows large, often climbing nearly to the tops of big forest trees. The large leaves are three- to five-lobed or entire, with

Summer Grape (Vitis aestivalis)

short broad teeth, and are whitish or rusty woolly beneath. The petioles are rather short, covered with downy hairs. The numerous fruits are in long dense clusters. The berries are from a quarter to nearly half an inch in diameter, black covered with a whitish bloom that gives them somewhat of a bluish appearance. This vine is native from New England to Florida and west to Wisconsin, Kansas, and Texas.

The fruit when ripe is pleasant, but the seeds are large for the size of the berry. When thoroughly ripe, it is excellent for eating and good for jellies or in pies. The berries are generally ripe in September or October but are sweeter after heavy frosts.

The grapes are very abundant in western Pennsylvania where I lived as a boy. Like most wild fruits, they are better and larger on some vines than on others. We knew all the good vines of the neighborhood. The best are often hard to reach, and those lines of James Whitcomb Riley's frequently applied to my case:

> the wild grape-vine
> That ust to climb the highest tree
> To keep the ripest ones fer me.[1]

The following species of wild grapes have vines and fruit very similar to the ones just described.

Blue or Winter Grape, Vitis bicolor, with longer, smoother petioles, and leaves bluish white beneath. New Hampshire to North Carolina, west to Michigan and Tennessee.

Sweet Winter Grape, or Downy Grape, Vitis cinerea, with angled branchlets and small fruit, black without bloom. Illinois to Kansas, south to Texas and east to Florida.

Riverside, Sweet-scented, or Frost Grape, Vitis vulpina, trailing or climbing, leaves shining and green both sides, usually three-lobed with large acute teeth, berries blue with a bloom and very juicy but sour. New Brunswick to North Dakota, south to Maryland and Kansas.

Sand or Sugar Grape, Vitis rupestris, low and bushy, often without tendrils, leaves small and shining, berries about one-fourth inch in diameter, in small close clusters, black with a bloom, sweet. Southern Pennsylvania to Tennessee and southward.

All the above species and the Chicken Grape, Vitis cordifolia, make a good quality of grape juice, and may be used for jelly.

---

[1] From "Neighborly Poems" by James Whitcomb Riley, copyright 1891, 1919. Used by special permission of the publishers, The Bobbs-Merrill Company.

MUSCADINE, SOUTHERN FOX GRAPE, OR BULLACE GRAPE

Vitis rotundifolia

Muscadinia rotundifolia

But O the glad September,
When the wind is in the pines,
And the gusty groves are sweetened
By the swaying muscadines! [1]

THIS vine usually trails on the ground or over bushes but sometimes climbs high in trees. The tendrils are unbranched, often few; leaves, rather small, nearly round, with large blunt teeth and shining on both sides. The clusters are small, but the berries are

Muscadine (Vitis rotundifolia)

[1] From "Comes One with a Song," by Frank L. Stanton, copyright 1898, 1925. Used by special permission of the publishers, The Bobbs-Merrill Company.

large, from one-half to three-fourths inch in diameter, purple without a bloom. The skin is thick and tough.

This grape ranges from Delaware to Kentucky and Kansas, and south to Florida and Texas. The fruit is pleasant to eat and excellent for jellies and pies. A good grape syrup may be made from it. The Scuppernong and some other southern cultivated grapes originated from this species. The fruit ripens early, and the berries fall from the cluster grape by grape. Those who are familiar with them when ripe will agree with John Henry Boner when he says:

> Pendent dewdrops glitter brightly
> In the overhanging vines,
> Laden with a luscious treasure
> Of large purple muscadines—
> Ripe delicious muscadines.

A similar species, Vitis Munsoniana, grows in sandy soil in Georgia and Florida. The vine is slender and low-climbing or trailing. The leaves are quite similar to those of the Muscadine. The berries are about half an inch in diameter or a little larger, nearly black, with a thin skin and without a musky taste. The plant is said to flower and fruit throughout the year.

George Catlin, author and artist, in his book *Illustrations of the Manners, Customs, and Condition of the North American Indians,* published in 1841, describes traveling a hundred years ago in what is now southern Oklahoma:

Scarcely a day passed, in which we have not crossed oak ridges of several miles in breadth, with a sandy soil and scattering timber; where the ground was almost literally covered with vines, producing the greatest profusion of delicious grapes, of five-eighths of an inch in diameter, and hanging in such endless clusters, as justly to entitle this singular and solitary wilderness to the style of a vineyard (and ready for the vintage), for many miles together.

The above lines may have been written about the Muscadine, but the habit of growth on oak ridges suits better another southern species, Vitis Linsecomii.

MUSTANG GRAPE
Vitis candicans

ANOTHER rapidly growing and high-climbing grape has leaves from two to five inches in diameter. They vary from nearly round or broader than long to triangular in outline with shallow teeth and occasionally with angular lobes. The leaves are smooth above but densely white woolly beneath. The berries are round, from half an inch to nearly an inch in diameter, or about the size of those of the Northern Fox Grape. They are dark purple or wine-colored with a tough skin. These grapes at their best are not edible, but they are often gathered for pies and jellies. This vine is a native of Texas, and its fruit ripens in June and July.

There are several other species of wild grapes found in the South, especially in Texas. Some of them have edible fruits, but the berries are small. One of these Vitis arizonica, found from Texas to Arizona, is believed to have been cultivated by the Pueblo Indians as the plants have been found growing in rows. It is today used by the Indians.

MAYPOP, OR PASSION FLOWER, OR PASSION VINE
Passiflora incarnata

ONE would scarcely think of the Passion Vine as bearing edible fruits, but that is the case.

This strong perennial vine grows to a length of fifteen to thirty feet, often covering bushes, generally low-climbing or trailing. Long tendrils, growing from the axils of the leaves, are the chief means of support. The three-lobed leaves are from three to five inches long, about as broad, with fine saw-toothed margins. The handsome flowers arise from the axils of the leaves, on peduncles or stems two or three inches long. The blossoms are about two inches in diameter; the sepals, four or five in number, are about an inch long, green without, tinged with lavender within. The white petals are the same number and size but much broader. Attached to the inside of these is a crown or fringe of purple or pink threadlike rays or filaments. The yellow edible berry is two inches or more long—about the size and shape of a hen's egg.

This vine is found in rather dry ground from Virginia to Florida, west to Missouri and Texas. I have collected it in Florida not far from the Gulf coast. The fruit is called Maypop by the people of the South and is often gathered and eaten. Captain John Smith said this plant was cultivated by the Indians of Virginia. He refers to the fruit as pleasant and wholesome. In parts of the South it is considered a noxious weed, from its rapid growth. The fruit is made into jelly, which is said to be of a superior quality. It is probably this vine that John Muir had in mind when he wrote of his trip on foot from Wisconsin to Texas. He called it Apricot Vine and said it had a superb flower and the most delicious fruit

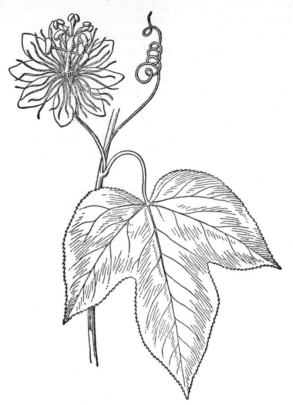

Passion Flower (Passiflora incarnata)

he had ever eaten. Like some of the edible tropical passion vines, the fruit could be used in making sherbets, and for preparing a refreshing drink.

YELLOW PASSION FLOWER
Passiflora lutea

THIS slender, rather delicate vine climbs up and over bushes often ten or twelve feet high. The leaves are broader than long, with three rounded lobes, entire margin, and slightly heart-shaped base. The tendrils are long, threadlike, and sensitive—the most beautiful to be found on any American plant of my acquaintance. The flower stems, two or three inches long, generally appear in pairs from the upper axils of the leaves. The greenish yellow flowers, scarcely an inch in diameter, are beautiful but not conspicuous. The dark purple fruits are round or slightly oblong, from a half to three-fourths of an inch in diameter.

The Yellow Passion Vine is found in thickets and on rich hillsides from Pennsylvania to Illinois and Kansas, and south to Florida and Texas. The pulpy fruit has a rich purple juice with a flavor peculiar to itself. One warm September day, I was collecting plants in a mountainous section of southern Pennsylvania and became tired and hungry. I chanced to come across some vines of this species containing ripe fruits. I was familiar with the vine, but it was the first opportunity that I had ever had to eat the fruits. They satisfied my hunger and quenched my thirst, but I would scarcely call them first-class. They may do for jelly and would surely make a pleasing drink.

There are numerous species of passion vines in the tropics. Some of these, such as the Giant Granadilla and Water Lemon, are grown for their fruits.

EASTERN PRICKLY PEAR, OR INDIAN FIG, OR PRICKLY PEAR CACTUS

Opuntia vulgaris

Opuntia Opuntia

THE Eastern Prickly Pear is a thickened, jointed, branching plant, sometimes a foot long, generally prostrate, occasionally ascending. The joints are oval or oblong, flat, from two to five inches long. The plants bear very tiny awl-shaped leaves which lie flat against the stem and generally drop early. The short bristles are greenish yellow. The grayish, sharp-pointed solitary spines are nearly an inch long. A majority of the plants do not bear spines. The yellow flowers are two or more inches broad with eight or ten petals and numerous stamens. The red pear-shaped fruits are an inch to an inch and a half long, fleshy, juicy, and edible.

This plant grows on rocks or in sand, generally near the coast, from Massachusetts to Florida and Alabama. Other similar edible species are found in Florida.

The fruits of the Prickly Pear have a pleasant taste and may be eaten fresh or stewed. I have seen them in the markets at New York and have collected them fresh from the plants—sometimes to my regret, for the spiny bristles are very annoying.

In the summer of 1936, the writer spent a few days in Montana when the terrible drought of that year was at its worst. The pas-

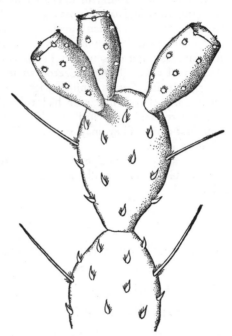

Eastern Prickly Pear (Opuntia vulgaris)

turage was burned brown, vegetables were scarce, and some of the inhabitants secured part of their diet from the Prickly Pear, or Tuna, Opuntia polyacantha. The new or tender joints were taken, the skin with prickles sliced off, and the remainder boiled, then fried or treated some other way. According to Dr. Frederick V. Coville, some of the cacti of the Southwest are eaten by the Indians. The Prickly Pear, Opuntia basilaris is one of these. Only the half-grown or tender joints are taken for this purpose. They are even dried for food.

WESTERN PRICKLY PEAR. DEVIL'S TONGUE

Opuntia Rafinesquii

Opuntia humifusa

THIS cactus is found in sandy or rocky soil from Ohio, Michigan,
to Minnesota and south to Texas. In many respects it is similar to
the eastern species; but the deep green joints are more oval or nearly

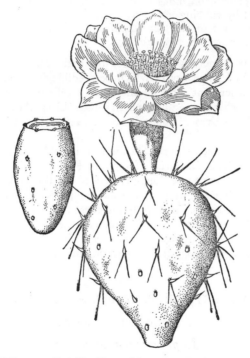

Western Prickly Pear (Opuntia Rafinesquii)

round, the bristles are reddish brown, and the spines are three or
four together, one of them being larger and stronger than the others.
Occasionally a plant is found without spines. The flowers are yellow, often with a reddish center, about three inches in diameter,
with ten or twelve petals. The fruits are an inch and a half to two
inches long, and about half as thick, filled with a purplish edible
pulp.

In his interesting contribution to the 1919 Report of the Bureau of American Ethnology, "Uses of Plants by Indians of the Missouri River Region," Melvin Randolph Gilmore says of this cactus:

The fruits were eaten fresh and raw after the bristles had been removed, or they were stewed. They were also dried for winter use. Sometimes from scarcity of food, the Indians had to resort to the stems, which they roasted after first removing the spines. The mucilaginous juice of the stems was utilized as a sizing to fix the colors painted on hides or on receptacles made from hides. It was applied by rubbing a freshly peeled stem over the painted object. On account of this mucilaginous property, the peeled stems were bound on wounds as a dressing.

There are numerous members of the great cactus family in the southwestern United States which bear edible fruits. I can testify from experience that some of these are excellent eating. Without doubt, the prickly pear and the chollas of the Great American Desert have saved the lives of many weary travelers far from food and water.

The Indian Fig, Opuntia ficus-indica, and Opuntia megacantha according to Dr. S. B. Parish of Jepson's *Flora of California,* "were in cultivation as fruit trees long previous to the discovery of America, and exhibit a diversity of variation comparable with that of the common cultivated fruits." I have found these two species at several of the old missions in southern California where they were planted one hundred and fifty years or more ago. The ovoid fleshy fruits, two to four inches long, are juicy with a pleasant taste.

BUFFALO BERRY, OR RABBIT BERRY, OR SILVERLEAF

Shepherdia argentea

Lepargyraea argentea

THE Buffalo Berry is a shrub that provides a common yet valuable wild fruit in the Northwest where cultivated fruits are scarce. It grows from five to fifteen feet high. The twigs often end in thorns. The opposite, oblong leaves have entire margins. They are an inch or two long, scarcely half as wide, covered with a dense silvery wool on both sides. The small, yellowish, dioecious flowers (the pistillate on one shrub, the staminate on another) open in April or May, and the scarlet or orange fruits ripen in July or August.

This hardy shrub is found native from Minnesota and Manitoba south and west to Kansas, New Mexico, Idaho, and California. The round or oblong fruits, about the size of currants, have a single, slender seed. They are acid but edible with a pleasant taste much like that of the red currant, are especially valuable for jelly, and are delicious for dessert when dried with sugar. The Indians dried the berries for winter use, and often cooked them with buffalo meat; hence the common name.

This wild fruit is now being cultivated in the cold Northwest, and we may expect it to improve. In the wild state it is very prolific,

Buffalo Berry (Shepherdia argentea)

the branches being thickly studded with fruits which remain on the bushes well into the winter.

Friends of the writer who live in Montana say that the Buffalo Berry produces better jelly than that obtained from any other fruit in the region. During the very dry summer of 1936, I found the Buffalo Berry along the Yellowstone River in eastern Montana, along the Little Missouri River in North Dakota, and in the Black Hills; but what little fruit remained on the bushes was being rapidly eaten by birds. I have not had a chance to test the edible qualities of the fruit.

George Catlin in his travels among the North American Indians, about 1833, describes the Buffalo Berry which then grew so abundantly about the mouth of the Yellowstone River:

The buffalo bushes (Shepherdia), which are peculiar to these northern regions, lined the banks of the river and defiles in the bluffs, sometimes for miles together; forming almost impassable hedges, so loaded with the weight of their fruit, that their boughs were everywhere gracefully bending down and resting on the ground.

This shrub which may be said to be the most beautiful ornament that decks out the wild prairies, forms a striking contrast to the rest of the foliage, from the blue appearance of its leaves, by which it can be distinguished for miles in distance. The fruit which it produces in such incredible profusion, hanging in clusters to every twig, is about the size of ordinary currants, and not unlike them in color and even in flavor; being exceedingly acid and almost unpalatable, until they are bitten by the frosts of autumn, when they are sweetened, and their flavor delicious; having to the taste much the character of grapes, and I am inclined to think, would produce excellent wine.

Catlin believed that two men could gather thirty bushels of these berries in a day. He continues:

We several times took a large mackinaw blanket which I had in the canoe, and spreading it on the ground under the bushes, where they were the most abundantly loaded with fruit, and by striking the stalk of the tree with a club, we received the whole contents of its branches in an instant on the blanket, which was taken up by the corners and not infrequently would produce us, from one blow, the eighth part of a bushel of this fruit; when the boughs, relieved of their burden, instantly flew up to their native position.

At another place, Catlin writes that when he was feasting with an Indian chief a bowl

was filled with a kind of paste or pudding made of the flour of the *pomme blanche,* as the French call it, a delicious turnip of the prairie, finely flavored with the buffalo berries, which are collected in great quantities in this country and used with divers dishes in cooking as we in civilized countries use dried currants, which they very much resemble.

We have described the *pomme blanche* under edible roots.

The Canadian Buffalo Berry, Shepherdia canadensis, is a similar but smaller shrub growing from northern United States far into Canada. I have tried its orange berries and found them sweetish but insipid.

The Silverberry, Elaeagnus argentea, is also a member of the oleaster family. It grows over much of Canada and comes as far south as the Dakotas. Its silvery mealy fruit is edible.

WINTERGREEN, CHECKERBERRY, BOXBERRY, PARTRIDGEBERRY, MOUNTAIN TEA, OR TEABERRY

Gaultheria procumbens

THE Wintergreen is a shrubby plant creeping upon or beneath the surface of the ground with erect branches from three to six inches high. The evergreen, aromatic leaves are usually clustered at the

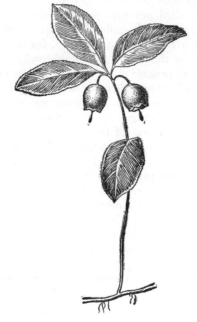

Wintergreen (gaultheria procumbens)

summit of the branches. The mature leaves are of a rigid or stiff texture, dark glossy green above, paler beneath, oval in outline with small bristle-tipped teeth.

The young leaves are light green or yellowish green, often with a reddish tinge. The nodding flowers on recurved stems are generally solitary in the axils of the leaves. The white bell-shaped corolla with its five lobes or teeth encloses the ten stamens. The calyx becomes fleshy, forming a small berrylike fruit which turns bright red and hangs on the stems all winter. Both the leaves and the berries have the pleasing spicy, aromatic flavor of Wintergreen or Sweet Birch.

This plant is found most often in wild, rough mountainous country, frequently under evergreens, from Newfoundland to Manitoba, and south to Georgia. No other wild plant led the writer into the woods so often as this one. Its mere name recalls many pleasant rambles afield for the leaves and berries. In early spring and sometimes during the winter when the ground was free from snow, we were pretty sure to find these berries in open sunny woods sloping to the south. We often filled our coat pockets with them, for they are quite firm and do not smash easily. We were sometimes startled by the whir of the partridge or ruffed grouse, for these birds are fond of the berries (hence the name "partridgeberry"). In some sections of Pennsylvania and perhaps elsewhere, the berries in the springtime are used for pies. I have seen them for sale in the city markets, where they command a good price. I have never seen them so large or so abundant as they are in some parts of Maine.

The young, tender leaves of the Wintergreen are very pleasant eating. The mature leaves are often eaten, but they are tougher and less agreeable. A very pleasing and refreshing tea is made by steeping the leaves for a few minutes in boiling water. In many parts of the country, the plants are used for this purpose. The common names Mountain Tea and Teaberry indicate this. When I was a youngster, I often induced Mother to make tea for me from the fresh leaves of this plant and much preferred it to the "store-bought" tea, especially when served with sugar and cream.

The Gaultheria, or Wintergreen, is one of the best known of all our wild American plants. Twenty-five common names given to it attest this fact.

BLACK HUCKLEBERRY, OR WHORTLEBERRY

Gaylussacia baccata

Gaylussacia resinosa

THIS shrub grows from one to three feet high, with numerous grayish brown rigid branches. The alternate leaves are oval or oblong with entire margins and very short petioles. The leaves, especially when young, and also the blossoms, contain many tiny resinous globules. The pinkish or pale red flowers are arranged in short one-sided racemes. The bell-shaped or cylindrical corolla has five short lobes. The ten stamens are generally a little shorter than the blossoms.

The round shiny black fruit is about a quarter of an inch in diameter and contains ten bony seedlike nutlets. The fruit is sweet and pleasantly flavored but more "seedy" than the blueberries.

Black Huckleberry (Gaylussacia baccata)

This shrub is found from Newfoundland to Georgia, west to Manitoba, Wisconsin, and Kentucky. It generally grows in dry, sandy, or rocky soil, often with the blueberries. The black huckleberries are usually gathered and mixed with the blueberries, but I have eaten excellent pie made from black huckleberries alone.

The Tangleberry, Dangleberry, or Blue Tangle, Gaylussacia frondosa, is a very similar shrub to the one described above. It bears fewer but larger berries on slender drooping stems. They are dark blue with a whitish bloom, sweet and pleasing to the taste. This shrub is found in moist woods and thickets from New Hampshire to Florida and Louisiana. While it generally occurs near the coast, it has been found as far west as Ohio.

MOUNTAIN OR ROCK CRANBERRY, OR COWBERRY,
OR LOW-BUSH CRANBERRY

Vaccinium Vitis-Idaea

Vitis-Idaea Vitis-Idaea

THE Cowberry is a little shrubby plant with creeping stems and upright branches from two to eight inches high. The leathery, evergreen leaves are dark green, smooth and shining above, paler and dotted with black points beneath. They are from one-fourth to three-fourths of an inch long, obovate or broader at the outer end, and the edges are generally rolled in. The petioles are very short. The small nodding flowers are white or pink, shaped like a bell, with four lobes, and are arranged on the plant in short terminal racemes. They appear in June and July. The dark red berries are ripe in August and September but cling to the plant all winter, even to the next summer. They are from a fourth- to a half-inch in diameter, or smaller than those of the American Cranberry, sour and slightly bitter.

This species is native of northern Europe, Asia, and America, extending north to the Arctic Ocean and south to Massachusetts, the Adirondacks and Lake Superior region. It grows in rather dry rocky soil, and the berries are apparently larger and better far north.

Like the cranberry, the fruit is not good raw but when properly sweetened is excellent for sauce and jelly. In fact, it is much used as a substitute for the cranberry. Seventy-five years ago, when Henry D. Thoreau, the naturalist, was exploring the Moosehead Lake region of Maine, he reported that the mountain cranberry, stewed and sweetened, was the common dessert in that sparsely populated region. It is much used in Nova Scotia, New Brunswick, and parts of Quebec. It is not cultivated, but fruits from the wild plants are gathered and sent to the Boston markets. It is highly prized in Europe, where the plants and berries grow slightly larger than they do in America. The berries are gathered in the Scandinavian countries and placed in tight barrels which are then filled with water and shipped to the New York markets. I have secured the berries in the markets and know that they are an excellent substitute for the cranberry.

The black bear in Canada and the polar bear on the Arctic coasts spend much time eating the fruits of this little evergreen plant, and at certain seasons it is an important food of northern birds.

HIGH-BUSH BLUEBERRY, OR SWAMP BLUEBERRY, OR WHORTLEBERRY

Vaccinium corymbosum

THIS shrub grows from three to fifteen feet high with stiff greenish brown branches. The oval or oblong leaves, on short petioles, are pointed at both ends. They are from an inch and a half to three inches long and about half as wide, with entire margins, green above, paler beneath. The five-toothed corolla is bell-shaped or cylindrical, white or pinkish, with ten stamens. The berries are from a quarter to a third of an inch in diameter, bluish black, with a bloom. When the bloom is rubbed off, they are almost black or, as Robert Frost the poet says of the Blueberry:

> After all really they're ebony skinned;
> The blue's but a mist from the breath of the wind,
> A tarnish that goes at a touch of the hand.[1]

This is the late-market blueberry. The fruit is ripe in July and August, and in late seasons some may be gathered in September. It generally grows in swamps, wet woods, and thickets, but in the great huckleberry region of western Massachusetts I have found them abundant in rather dry old pastures. The geographic range of the wild fruit is from Maine to Minnesota, south to Virginia and Louisiana. It is apparently most abundant east of the mountains. In the swampy lands of Connecticut and New Jersey, I have seen bushes nearly fifteen feet high laden with berries. It is recorded that one picker in the latter state filled an entire crate with the fruit of one bush. This wild fruit was much used in colonial times, and the Indians cooked it with meat, often drying it for this purpose.

There are fifteen or twenty species of blueberries (Vaccinium) in the United States east of the plains. The exact species are often difficult to determine; but none of them is poisonous, although some are not edible. One species, *Vaccinium stamineum,* known as Deerberry and Squaw Huckleberry, has fruit round or slightly pear-shaped, sometimes half an inch in diameter, green or greenish yellow when ripe, and is sour and inedible. One author says, "No creature, unless hard pressed by hunger, could relish the greenish

[1] "Blueberries" from "North of Boston" by Robert Frost. Used by special permission of the publishers, Henry Holt and Company.

or yellowish berries." Yet, I am assured by people living in the mountains of Pennsylvania that, after being stewed and properly sweetened, they make excellent pies. I have not tried them, but we must not forget that the cranberry is inedible raw. The deerberry bushes grow two or three feet high, and the dangling berries are produced in abundance. It is native from Massachusetts to Minnesota, south to Florida, Kentucky, and Louisiana.

As yet the blueberries have been cultivated very little, probably because they require a peculiar acid soil, but the late Dr. Frederick V. Coville, United States Government Botanist, experimented with them and produced berries of remarkable size. The time will probably come when the blueberries will be among our cherished cultivated fruits. Berries of cultivated varieties are now seen in the markets.

LOW SWEET BLUEBERRY, OR LOW-BUSH BLUEBERRY, OR DWARF, SUGAR, OR EARLY SWEET BLUEBERRY

Vaccinium pennsylvanicum

Vaccinium angustifolium

THIS is the early-market blueberry, ripening in June and July or, farther north, in August. The bushes rarely grow more than twenty inches high and often not half that. The branches are green and warty, with alternate oblong or lanceolate leaves, bright green and shining on both sides. The white or pinkish corolla is oblong bell-shaped. The berries on short stems are blue with a bloom, very sweet and pleasant. Like all blueberries, they vary greatly in size, ranging from a quarter of an inch to nearly half an inch in diameter. It grows in dry sandy or rocky soil from Newfoundland to Saskatchewan, south to Virginia and Illinois. I have never seen this species grow to such perfection or so abundantly as on the mountains of Maine and in some parts of Massachusetts; but the poet Robert Frost, of the latter state, apparently had seen larger ones when he wrote in his poem "Blueberries,"

> Blueberries as big as the end of your thumb,
> Real sky-blue, and heavy, and ready to drum
> In the cavernous pail of the first one to come!

This is one of our finest wild fruits, sweet and juicy, valuable for pies, puddings, and desserts in general. The Indians were especially fond of it, and because of its abundance it was a very important article in their diet. On July 30, 1831, Henry Schoolcraft, the noted authority on the habits and customs of the Indians, while traveling down the Namokagum River in northwestern Wisconsin wrote in his journal: "Both banks of the river are literally covered with the ripe whortleberry—it is large and delicious. The Indians feast on it. Thousands on thousands of bushels of this fruit could be gathered with little labor. It is seen in the dried state at every lodge. All the careful Indian housewives dry it. It is used as a seasoning to soups." A month later, while still on this tributary of the St. Croix, he writes of the Indians: "Their first request is tobacco, although they are half starved, and have lived on nothing but whortleberries for weeks." Later, when wild fowl came to the neighborhood, the Indians fared better; and Schoolcraft wrote: "Pieces of duck were thrown in a large kettle of boiling water, which was thickened with whortleberries, for the family supper."

There is much confusion as to the names "whortleberry," "blueberry," and "huckleberry." "Whortleberry" is an old name applied chiefly to an English species and once used for nearly all our native species, now rarely heard. "Blueberry" is applied to the high and low species east of the Appalachian Mountains. In and west of these mountains, the name "huckleberry" is applied to all species.

Nearly a dozen species of blueberries are found in the Pacific states. They are nearly all gathered for food and are used by whites and Indians alike.

BLUE HUCKLEBERRY, OR LATE LOW BLUEBERRY
Vaccinium vacillans

THIS shrub in some respects is quite similar to the last. It is larger, attaining a height of one to three feet, with yellowish green warty branches and twigs. The oval leaves are from one to two inches long and a little more than half as wide, pale above, and pale whitish beneath, finely veined. The leaf margins are generally smooth, but sometimes minutely saw-toothed. The flowers usually occur in small clusters but sometimes in racemes on naked branches. The corolla is about one-fourth of an inch long, yellowish or sometimes with a reddish tinge. The berries are similar to those of the last named species, but are generally a little smaller. They are dark blue with a bloom. This excellent blueberry is found from New England to Michigan, south to North Carolina and Missouri. It grows in woodlands in rather dry, sandy, or rocky soil, and the berries ripen in July and August. It is especially common in the Allegheny plateau region of western Pennsylvania and West Virginia where it is called huckleberry.

This species is the chief blueberry or huckleberry of my boyhood, and what pleasant recollections I have of going berrying! Those who only eat huckleberry pie and puddings in their homes or at hotels and restaurants have missed half the joy connected with these wild fruits. As I look back through the years, I seem to have a more pleasant and vivid recollection of gathering huckleberries than I have of eating pies and puddings. With pails and tin cups we sallied forth to the huckleberry patches in woods and open thickets, each boy picking the berries in his cup and then emptying them in his pail, which was safely hidden beneath a spreading bush or under a low-branching tree. We did not starve either while gathering them, for the boys were as full as the pails they proudly carried home.

Since writing the foregoing lines, I came across this sentiment expressed by Margaret Fishback, poetess of New York:

> Owing to sentimentality,
> Blueberry muffins appeal to me.
>
> It isn't their taste I like at all.
> It's only the summers they recall—
>
> Summers of adolescent ease,
> Gingham dresses and scrubby knees.
>
> The muffins repelled me even then,
> But holidays and the age of ten
>
> Are very pleasant to munch on now,
> So pass me another anyhow.[1]

LARGE OR AMERICAN CRANBERRY

Vaccinium macrocarpon

Oxycoccus macrocarpus

WHILE we are all familiar with cranberries as they appear on the stalls of the markets or in boxes and barrels in the grocery and vegetable stores, and we know the cranberry sauce that is served with the

---

[1] "Flashback" from "I Take It Back" by Margaret Fishback, published and copyrighted by E. P. Dutton & Co., Inc., New York.

Thanksgiving turkey, yet very few are acquainted with the wild
cranberry growing in its native home in the bogs and marshes of
northeastern United States.

This slender creeping vine grows from six inches to two feet long,
branches ascending, with alternate, oval, or oblong entire evergreen
leaves, about half an inch long, green above and light or whitish
beneath. The pale rose-colored nodding flowers are about one-third
of an inch across, divided almost to the base into four petal-like segments. The oblong or nearly round berries are at first green, but in
September or October they turn red. They are from two-fifths to
three-fourths of an inch long, but in cultivation they often become
larger. The berries are firm, and when well protected by snow ofteii
remain on the vines all winter. The cranberries are not eaten as fresh
fruit; but when stewed with a bountiful supply of sugar they make
delicious sauce and jelly.

This wild fruit is native in open bogs and marshes from Newfoundland to western Ontario, south to Virginia and Arkansas.
Some of the berries that we see in the markets have been gathered
from the wild plants especially in Michigan and Wisconsin. The
majority of the market berries have been obtained by cultivation
especially in the Cape Cod district and from south Jersey and Wisconsin. Thousands of acres are under cultivation for this purpose.
Low boggy land with a peat bottom is generally selected, and in
winter the areas are flooded. Under cultivation the berries are
usually larger, and the plants more productive.

In lowlands among the sand dunes of Cape Cod, I have seen
areas of a few square rods, any one of which had more than enough
wild berries to serve a family. In early days the entire supply came
from wild plants.

The history of the cranberry is interesting. It is believed that the
Pilgrims learned from the Indians how to prepare the fruit for the
table. The berries kept so long without decay and were prized so
highly by the colonists that, according to the early history of Massachusetts, ten barrels of them were shipped across the ocean as a gift
to King Charles II, a long journey in slow-moving sailing vessels.
The colonists called the vine "craneberry" because the blossoms are
shaped like the head and neck of a crane. The word was shortened
later to "cranberry."

Colonel James Smith, who was captured by the French and Indians at Fort Duquesne in 1755, lived with the savages in Ohio and
Michigan from that year to 1859. Smith later wrote that the Indians had many apples (wild crab apples) stored up. Here too he

saw for the first time "cranberries which grew in swamps and were gathered by the Indians when the swamps were frozen. These berries were about as large as rifle bullets, of a bright red color and of agreeable flavor, though rather too sour of themselves, but when mixed with sugar, had a very agreeable taste."

This fruit has been cultivated for a hundred years. The crop has increased until it is now over six hundred thousand barrels annually. With skillful cultivation, it is claimed, the cranberry grower may get one hundred and fifty bushels to the acre. Cranberry juice, sweetened and used alone or mixed with other fruit juices, is becoming a popular appetizer. Besides cranberry jelly, sauce, and pie, there are many other uses for this fruit, as in muffins, pudding, ice cream, sherbet, cookies, and tarts.

The Small, or European, Cranberry (Vaccinium Oxycoccos, *Oxycoccus Oxycoccos*) of some authors, is native to northern Europe and Asia and also to the northern part of this country over much the same area as the larger species except that west of the mountains it does not extend as far south. The whole plant is very similar to the Large Cranberry but is smaller in almost every respect, even to the fruit.

CREEPING SNOWBERRY, OR IVORY PLUM

Chiogenes hispidula

THIS slender branching vine grows to the length of fifteen to twenty inches. The brownish stems creep close to the ground. The small, alternate, oval leaves are two-ranked, short-petioled, less than half an inch long, pointed, rounded at the base, dark glossy green above, brownish beneath. The margins of the leaves are entire and slightly turned under. The small white bell-shaped flowers are solitary in the axils of the leaves. The pure white oblong berries are borne on small recurved stems. Both the leaves and the berries have the aroma of wintergreen. The berries may be gathered in August and September.

The Creeping Snowberry is found from Labrador to British Columbia, south to North Carolina, Michigan, and Minnesota. It generally grows in peat bogs and low mossy woods but is sometimes found in dry shady soil, even creeping over decayed logs. The leaves lie flat on the ground and seem to be held there by the rough hairs on the underside.

The berries are never abundant, but in Maine and also in the upper

peninsula of Michigan I have gathered hand-
fuls of them and enjoyed the delicate wintergreen flavor and slightly acid taste. I consider it the most ethereal of all our wild
fruits. The stems and leaves when steeped
make a refreshing tea for the tired camper.
Henry D. Thoreau, the naturalist, while
camping in Maine years ago, recorded in his
journal that his Indian guide returned from
a short walk with a plant of this species in
his hand, saying that it made the best tea of
anything in the woods. He goes on to say:
"We determined to have some tea made of
this tonight. It had a slight checkerberry
flavor, and we both agreed that it was really
better than the black tea which we had
brought. We thought it quite a discovery and
that it might well be dried and sold in the
shops."

Neltje Blanchan says of this plant: "Al-
lied on the one hand to the cranberry, so
often found with it in the cool northern peat
bogs, and on the other to the delicious blueberries, this 'snow-born' berry which appears
on no dining table, nevertheless furnishes
many a good meal to hungry birds and fagged
pedestrians."

Creeping Snowberry
(Chiogenes hispidula)

PERSIMMON, OR DATE PLUM

Diospyros virginiana

Have you ever
On your travels
Through the queer, uncertain South,
Had a 'simmon—
Green persimmon—
Make a sortie on your mouth?
—Frank H. Sweet

THE persimmon is generally a small straight-growing tree, sometimes reaching a height of eighty feet and a diameter of twenty inches.
The bark is hard, dark, and deeply furrowed. The leaves are oval,
pointed, rather thick, downy when young but later becoming smooth.

The petioles are short, and the leaves often fall early. The four-parted, cream-colored flowers are of two types. The sterile form, or those that contain only stamens, are generally clustered and are about one-fourth of an inch across; and in these the number of stamens is sixteen. The fertile flowers, or those with both pistil and stamens, are twice as large, solitary, and contain eight stamens, sometimes fewer.

The round fruit is an inch to an inch and a half in diameter, orange-colored when ripe, with several large flat seeds. It is very

Persimmon (Diospyros virginiana)

astringent when green but sweet and edible when ripe, especially after frost.

The persimmon is found from Connecticut to Iowa and Kansas, south to Florida and Texas. The tree seems to reach its finest development in the Ohio valley and southwest in Oklahoma.

Much difference of opinion prevails as to the quality of the fruit. Most manuals say that after frost it is sweet and luscious, but in one prominent text we read "sweet and sometimes edible after exposure to frost." Perhaps the author had the experience of tasting unripe persimmons. The fruit varies wonderfully as to both size and flavor. Occasionally a tree is found whose fruit is never palatable, regardless of freezing. I have known trees in the Ohio valley that bore delicious fruit in early October even before the first frost. One writer refers to ripe persimmons as "soft sugar lumps of fruit."

Dr. Charles C. Abbott glories in the persimmon, praising its color and taste, especially because it is best after all other wild fruits have been gathered. He says: "Does not the persimmon smack of the wild-wood? How little of the tamed orchard or trim garden in its sugary pulp! The town and all that that means is for the moment forgotten, and you are in touch with Nature while you eat."

Persimmon bread was often used by the early settlers in regions where this fruit abounds. One author speaks of it as superior to gingerbread. The custom of mixing ripe persimmons with the meal in making cakes was probably learned from the Indians.

The Japanese persimmon, Diospyros Kaki, is the best native fruit of that country. Many varieties of it have been developed, some of which are cultivated in the southern United States. The American persimmon is often seen in the markets of the South, but very little attention has been given to its cultivation and improvement. William Cullen Bryant, the poet, greatly admired it and believed that with proper selection it might become a valuable American fruit.

The Black, or Mexican, Persimmon, Diospyros texana, is native of southern Texas and northern Mexico. The tree is smaller than the northern species with a smoother gray bark. The fruit is about an inch in diameter, nearly black. I saw a tree in southern Texas that was ten inches in diameter. Its fruit was described as luscious.

GROUND CHERRY, OR STRAWBERRY TOMATO

Physalis pubescens

THIS annual plant when mature is about a foot high but spreads widely, its branches often resting on the ground. The entire plant is usually covered with soft short hairs. The nodes or joints are generally slightly swollen. The leaves are entire or sometimes slightly lobed. The blossom is between wheel-shape and funnel-form, about one-third of an inch across, yellow with a dark center. It has five closely packed stamens. After blossoming, the thin papery calyx becomes greatly enlarged, entirely enclosing the globular berry.

This ground cherry grows from New York and Pennsylvania southwest and south to the tropics. It is probably not native in the northern part of its range as it often escapes from cultivation. It especially adapts itself to new ground—that is, land that has been recently cleared and cultivated. There are two or three species of ground cherries with edible fruits that closely resemble one another and have been much confused by botanists.

The plant is a rapid grower and is often found in cornfields, developing after cultivation has ceased. The berries drop to the ground before they are ready to eat; but in a week or two the husk dries and the fruit within turns a golden yellow. It is then very sweet and pleasant, but not sticky or glutinous. The plants are prolific, and the berries will keep for weeks in the husk. They are excellent for preserves and sauce, and I have eaten wonderful pies made from them. Sometimes the berries are found for sale in the city markets. I agree with Dr. L. H. Bailey when he says: "The plant is worthy a place in every home garden."

The ground cherry has probably been in cultivation for a hundred and fifty years, yet I doubt if any serious attempts have ever been made to improve it.

The fruit of this plant has always been a favorite with the author. I recall an incident that occurred when I was probably seven years old. One morning my sister and I disobeyed, went to the dairy house and got into mischief. For fear of punishment (which as we later learned would not have been inflicted) we fled to a near-by cornfield. When noontime came, we hunted up ground cherries, which were just at their best, and ate to our satisfaction. In the afternoon we again filled up on the delicious berries. As night came on, the fear of darkness was greater than that of punishment, and we went noise‐lessly back to the house, perhaps frightened but not hungry.

The Tomatillo, or Mexican Ground Cherry, Physalis ixocarpa, is another edible species. The large purple berry often bursts the husk. It is found from New York to Texas and California, where it has escaped from cultivation.

BOXTHORN

Lycium carolinianum

THE Lycium, or Boxthorn, is a spiny spreading shrub from one to three feet tall. The alternate leaves are scarcely more than half an inch long, club-shaped or slightly broader above the middle, quite thick and fleshy. They are generally clustered and more numerous on the lateral branches. The flowers are small, purplish, broadly funnel-shaped, four or five cleft. The bright red berries are from a third- to a half-inch in diameter, slightly oblong, and edible.

The Lycium grows in sandy soil, mostly near the coast, from South Carolina to Florida and Texas. The calyx remains on the berry, giv-

ing it the appearance of a very small tomato. Both the Tomato and
the Boxthorn belong to the Potato family.

A correspondent from Texas writes concerning this plant: "The
berries of the Carolina Lycium have numerous small seeds and not
much pulp. It is pleasant eating, and is the only berry or fruit that I
know of that has a slightly salty taste. The Lycium comes in after
all other fruits are past. The bushes are hanging full now (December 16th) and I have seen them hanging ripe all winter."

There are several species of Lycium in New Mexico. The fruits
of practically all of them are eaten by the Indians.

PARTRIDGE BERRY, OR TWINBERRY
Mitchella repens

THE Partridge Berry, or Partridge Vine as it is often called, is
one of the most beautiful and unique of all our wild flowers. It must
be familiar to a great many people, too, for a score or more of common names have been applied to it. It is a slender, trailing, evergreen
plant, clinging closely to the ground and tak-
ing root at the nodes. The opposite, glossy
leaves, on short petioles, are ovate or heart-
shaped, and smooth on the edges. They are
generally about half an inch long, sometimes
larger, but often smaller, occasionally with
white veins. The flowers occur in pairs, terminal or in the axils of the leaves. The small
calyx is four-toothed. The corolla consists of
a slender tube half an inch long, with four
spreading lobes. The flowers are white or
pinkish and fragrant. In some plants, the
stamens extend beyond the corolla and the
pistil is shorter than the tube. In others, the
stamens are short and the pistil extends beyond the flower. This is one of Nature's de-
vices to secure cross-pollination. The twin

Partridge Berry
(Mitchella repens)

flowers are so united at the base that it takes the two blossoms to
form one berry. The poet Isaac Bassett Choate has well expressed
this:

> Made glad with springtime fancies pearly white,
> Two tender blossoms on a single stem

In their sweet coral fruitage close unite
As round bead cut from a garnet red.

The Partridge Berry is found from Nova Scotia to Minnesota, south to Florida and Texas. It is especially common in pine forests. The bright red berries are edible and hang on the vines all winter. In fact, the plant with its evergreen leaves is most conspicuous in winter if the ground is free from snow. The berries are about a quarter of an inch in diameter. They are never numerous but are pleasant and slightly aromatic. They cannot be gathered in quantity, but I like to eat a few on my rambles through the woods. They are food for wild birds, especially in winter and early spring when they often have trouble to find enough to eat. John Burroughs, in one of his poems, speaks of the plant thus:

Mitchella with her floral twins,
Crimson fruit that partridge wins.[1]

AMERICAN OR SWEET ELDER, OR ELDERBERRY

Sambucus canadensis

THE American Elder is a shrub that grows from five feet to twelve feet tall, sometimes two or three inches in diameter, but generally smaller. In the South, it is much larger—almost treelike. As a general thing, the upright stems grow in clusters from a mass of tangled roots, often lining fence rows, roadsides, about buildings and in out-of-the-way places, from Nova Scotia to Manitoba, south to Florida and Texas.

The young stems have greenish bark and very little wood; within is a cylinder of white pith. As the shrubs grow larger, the bark becomes grayish brown, the wood thicker, and the pith smaller. The opposite leaves are pinnately compound with from five to eleven leaflets. The lower leaflets are often lobed. The petioles are enlarged at the base, almost clasping the stem.

The broad flat flower clusters are sometimes eight inches across. The shrubs are a pleasing sight when in bloom. The individual flowers are about a quarter of an inch in diameter, star-shaped, creamy white and rather pleasantly scented. The blossoms appear in June and July.

[1] From "Bird and Bough" by John Burroughs. Special permission of the publishers, Houghton Mifflin Company.

In late summer and early autumn, the bushes are often bent with their load of fruit. The berries are round, deep purple or nearly black, sometimes nearly a quarter of an inch in diameter, very juicy, with three or four rough seeds. The fruit is often made into pies, jellies, and jams, but they are not acid enough to be very palatable.

Elderberry (Sambucus canadensis)

They are best when mixed with other fruits. The fresh flowers are sometimes mixed with batter and baked into cakes.

The Red-Berried Elder, Sambucus racemosa, with its conical clusters of early white flowers is common in mountainous sections of northeastern United States. The bright scarlet berries are bitter and unpleasant, but birds seem to enjoy them and often strip the bushes before the American Elder comes in bloom.

The Blue-Berried Elder, Sambucus glauca, is a tree that is said to reach a height of forty-five feet. It occurs from Utah to California, north to Montana and Vancouver. The fruit is larger than that of the eastern species, bluish black with a whitish bloom. It is sweet and juicy and is much used for pies and jellies. Without doubt, it was an important food of the American Indian. The tree is planted for ornament on the Pacific Coast.

HOBBLEBUSH, OR AMERICAN WAYFARING TREE
Viburnum alnifolium

THE Hobblebush is a spreading, branching shrub from three to ten feet high. The grayish purple branches are sometimes almost flat on the ground. These often take root at the ends or nodes, and when the passer-by catches his foot on a branch he is apt to take a tumble; hence the common names of Hobblebush, Trip-Toe, and Tanglefoot.

Like all the other Viburnums, this shrub has opposite leaves. In this species they are large (from three to eight inches across), nearly round, with pointed apex and heart-shaped base. The petioles are short, the veins prominent, and the edges of the blades are finely saw-toothed. The leaves become bronze in autumn, later turning to red. The flat flower clusters are from three to five inches broad. The white flowers are in the form of five-pointed stars. That is, the corolla is five-lobed; the calyx is five-toothed, and there are five stamens. Some of the flowers are sterile; these are nearly an inch broad and are on long stems. The fertile flowers, on short stems, are small. The slightly oblong berry is at first red, later turning to dark purple. The stone has three grooves on one side, one on the other.

The Hobblebush is native from New Brunswick to North Carolina, west to Ontario, Michigan, and Tennessee. I find it most common in mountainous regions. The fruit when ripe is sweet and edible. In the dense woods I have not often found it in fruit, but in more exposed situations the shrubs sometimes bear well. Birds are fond of the edible berries and do not always allow them to ripen.

CRANBERRY TREE, OR HIGH-BUSH CRANBERRY, OR PIMBINA
Viburnum Opulus

THIS handsome shrub is found in America from Newfoundland to British Columbia, and south to New Jersey, Iowa, and Oregon. It is also native to northern Europe and Asia Some botanists consider the American shrub only a variety of the European form. It generally grows six to ten feet high with quite erect grayish branches. The opposite leaves are about as broad as long, three-veined and three-lobed. The lobes and coarse teeth are pointed. The white flower clusters are three or four inches across. The marginal blossoms, with broad flat lobes nearly an inch in diameter, are sterile. The fertile flowers are much smaller. The shrubs bloom in May or June, but some seasons not until July. The fruit is nearly round or slightly oval, about a third of an inch in diameter, very sour, and slightly bitter. The stone is flat, nearly circular, not grooved. The bright red berries hang on the bushes all winter. They are eaten by our winter birds, but these rarely touch them until all other wild fruits are gone. In many places the fruit is used as a substitute for cranberries. E. P. Powell, in his volume *The Orchard and Fruit Garden,* says: "The fruit is very seldom used by human beings; but it makes excellent jelly, and a sauce fully as good as that from the real cranberry." It is much cultivated for ornament and is a good shrub for lawn or park.

The Cranberry Tree is the parent of the cultivated Snowball. By selection, the entire plant has been made to produce only sterile flowers, forming the well known clusters of the Snowball Bush of lawn and garden.

A much smaller but very similar shrub, Viburnum pauciflorum, also produces sour red berries which are used as a substitute for the cranberry. This shrub has a more northern range than the Cranberry Tree.

SWEET VIBURNUM, OR NANNYBERRY, OR WILD RAISIN

Viburnum Lentago

THE Sweet Viburnum is a shrub or small tree occasionally twenty-five feet high with numerous spreading branches. The leaves are from two to four inches long and about half as wide. The base is rounded, the apex long-pointed, and the margins close-set with small sharp teeth. The petioles, which are nearly an inch long, are wing-margined, which distinguishes this from other viburnums. The sessile flower clusters are from two to four inches broad. The white flowers are small and numerous, making the bushes beautiful in bloom.

The fruits are oblong or ovoid, bluish black with a bloom. The stones are circular or oval and flat. The fruits vary greatly in size and quality. Sometimes they are half an inch long, pulpy, very sweet, somewhat juicy, and pleasant to the taste. It is said that they were an important food of the Indians, but they did not dry them for winter use. The Sweet Viburnum appears in many catalogues of nurserymen, but only as a decorative shrub. So far as I am aware, no serious attempt has been made to improve the fruit, which is worthy of the best efforts of the horticulturist. It grows wild from Quebec to Hudson Bay and Manitoba, south to New Jersey, Indiana, and Kansas, and in the mountains as far as Georgia. It prefers a rich but moist soil. The fruit is ripe in September and October.

The Withe-Rod, or Appalachian Tea, Viburnum cassinoides, also has bluish black fruits that are sweet and edible. Its dried leaves have been used for tea. It is sometimes called False Paraguay Tea. It grows from Newfoundland to Manitoba, south to Georgia and Alabama.

The Larger Withe Rod, Viburnum nudum, has sweet edible fruits. It grows from Connecticut to Kentucky, south to Florida and Texas.

BLACK HAW, OR STAGBUSH

Viburnum prunifolium

THIS is a shrub or small tree in many respects quite similar to the preceding species, but the leaves are very different. Those of the Black Haw are much smaller, generally only an inch or two long, narrowed at the base, obtuse or rather blunt-pointed, the edges finely saw-toothed. In some respects they resemble those of the plum tree, as the specific name suggests. The white flower clusters are from two to four inches broad and appear as the leaves are unfolding. The fruit becomes bright red, later changing to blue-black with a bloom. It is much the size and shape of that of the last species, perhaps a little smaller.

The Black Haw generally grows in dry soil on hillsides, open thickets, along fences and roadsides. Occasionally it may be found in moist situations. It is native from Connecticut, Michigan, and Kansas, south to Georgia and Texas.

The fruit of the Black Haw was a favorite with the writer and his companions during boyhood. We knew all the bushes for a mile around. Some bore large pulpy fruits, and those we visited every year. During the long noon hour at school, in October and November or even later in the season, we frequently visited a large spreading bush that grew along an old rail fence. It was almost the dimensions of a tree and bore fruit in abundance—the finest to be found in the neighborhood. After eating all the berries we wished, we frequently put some in our pockets to nibble at on our way back to school.

One author states that the berries "become edible after being touched by the frost." But frost is not necessary. In the southern

Black Haw (Viburnum prunifolium)

part of their range they are often ripe and sweet long before the first frost appears. I also find it stated that they are good to eat if one is very hungry. That author probably never ate black haws at their best. Every year I take rambles in quest of black haws and enjoy them now apparently with the same relish as in the days of my youth. I do not recall any other wild fruit that I enjoy more. Many wild fruits are easier and more graceful to eat. The black haw is more appreciated in and west of the mountains than it is east of them. An intelligent woman from West Virginia told the writer recently that, of all the wild fruits of her acquaintance, she considered black haws the best, not as a dessert in the home, but to eat fresh out of doors, just as they are gathered from the bush. Certainly no wild fruits are sweeter than the sweet viburnum and the black haw. This is well put by the poet James Whitcomb Riley in his lines:

> Ah! will any minstrel say,
> In his sweetest roundelay,
> What is sweeter, after all,
> Than black haws, in early Fall?—
> Fruit so sweet the frost first sat,
> Dainty-toothed, and nibbled at! [1]

ADDITIONAL SPECIES OF EDIBLE BERRIES

CALIFORNIA Juniper, Juniperus occidentalis, and other species of western junipers have berries that are often eaten by the Indians. Sometimes the fruits are ground and made into cakes.

California Fan Palm, Washingtonia filifera. Growing around the north and west sides of the Colorado Desert in southern California we find colonies of the native fan palm. Some reach a height of sixty to seventy feet, and usually the taller ones have all the lower leaves burned off so that the native Indians could better climb up to the fruit. Several clusters of fruit develop weighing about ten pounds each. The black oval berries are scarcely more than a quarter of an inch long, with pulp rather thin, seeds quite large. The Indians ate the fleshy pulp, then ground the seeds into a meal which Dr. Palmer thought as good as coconut.

False Solomon's-Seal, or False Spikenard, Smilacina racemosa, *Vagnera racemosa*. The False Solomon Seal is found from Nova Scotia to British Columbia, south to Georgia, Missouri, and Arizona. The aromatic berries are sometimes eaten. They are ripe in autumn.

Carrion Flower, or Jacob's Ladder, Smilax herbacea, ranges from New Brunswick to Manitoba, south to Florida and Oklahoma. The blue-black berries were eaten by Omaha Indians for their pleasant flavor. Other species of smilax have agreeable berries from which possibly jellies could be made. They are ripe in autumn and winter.

Oregon Grape, Berberis aquifolium, *Odostemon aquifolium,* is found from the Rocky Mountains to the Pacific Coast and is the floral emblem of Oregon. The leaves are evergreen, and the dark blue berries form in clusters, resembling small grapes. They are

---

[1] From "Rhymes of Childhood" by James Whitcomb Riley, copyright 1890, 1918. Used by special permission of the publishers. The Bobbs-Merrill Company.

eaten and used for jellies, also for making a beverage. The berries
ripen in autumn.

Red-Fruited Barberry, Berberis haematocarpa, *Odostemon ha-
ematocarpus,* is native of New Mexico and Arizona. "The berries
are bright blood red, pleasantly acid to the taste, and are used for
making jellies" (Wooton and Standley).

Sweetbrier, Rosa rubiginosa, native of Europe and Asia, is now
found in America in thickets, old fields, and along roadsides from
Nova Scotia to Ontario, south to Virginia, Tennessee, and Kansas.
The berries are gathered and sold in Norway. The hips of the native
wild roses were often eaten by the Indians. The hips of the Sweetbrier and those of native species are sometimes used for making jelly.
They are ripe in autumn.

Mountain Ash or Rowan Tree, Sorbus Aucuparia. The European Mountain Ash is much planted in this country and sometimes
escapes. Its large clusters of bright red fruits are used for making
marmalade in Scotland. The fruits of the American species, Sorbus
americana and Sorbus scopulina, which are quite like the European
species, could probably be used for the same purpose.

Christmas Berry, or California Holly, or Toyon, Photinia ar-
butifolia. This beautiful evergreen shrub found growing on the
lower mountain slopes, foothills, and in cañons from northern California to Mexico, has beautiful clusters of bright red fruit. The
berries are prized by the Indians, who eat them raw or roasted. They
cling to the bushes well into winter.

Giant Cactus, or Suwarro, Cereus giganteus. Like many other
species of cacti the red or purple fruits of the Giant Cactus of
Arizona are edible. Preserves are made from this species, also a
crude form of molasses.

Bunchberry, or Dwarf Cornel, Cornus canadensis, *Chamaeperi-
clymenum canadense.* The scarlet fruits of the Bunchberry are
edible, but to me they are somewhat insipid or tasteless. According to
G. B. Emerson, they are sometimes made into puddings. Newfoundland to Alaska, south to New Jersey, West Virginia, to
Colorado and California. I find this species abundant in the higher
Catskill Mountains. Said to have been eaten by the Indians. Berries
are ripe in late summer.

Sour Gum, or Black Gum, or Pepperidge, or Tupelo, Nyssa
sylvatica, *Nyssa multiflora.* This tree grows from Maine to Michigan, south to Florida and Texas. It is usually found in lowlands.
The acid fruits are greedily eaten by birds, and it is claimed that
they are sometimes used for preserves.

Large Tupelo, or Wild Olive, Nyssa aquatica, *Nyssa uniflora.* The Large Tupelo grows in swampy regions from Virginia to Missouri, south to Florida and Texas. The dark blue fruits when ripe are about an inch long and, according to Browne, are sold in the Savannah markets under the name of Ogeechee Lime. They are used for making a preserve.

Manzanita, Arctostaphylos Manzanita. This and other species of Manzanita, common to the mountains of the Pacific Coast, bear red berries that are in demand for making jelly. The manzanitas are closely related to the blueberries of the East. Dr. H. M. Hall says of this species: "The berries, which have an agreeable acid taste, are much prized by summer campers who utilize them in making a manzanita jelly." Dr. Hall again writes of the fruit of a similar species, the Green Manzanita, Arctostaphylos patula: "The ripening berries are pleasingly acid, the taste being similar to that of green apples." The name Manzanita is Spanish for "little apple." The Indians also use the berries for making cider. I have gathered the Manzanita berries in the Sierra Nevada Mountains and have found them agreeable but somewhat dry or mealy.

The familiar Bearberry Arctostaphylos, Uva-Ursi, *Uva-Ursi Uva-Ursi,* has fruit similar to that of the Manzanita. It is quite dry and insipid, but I should not be surprised if jelly could be made from it. It is found from New Jersey to Missouri and California, north.

The Western Wintergreen, Gaultheria shallon, is a Pacific Coast species from British Columbia to central California. The fruits, which are much esteemed by the Indians, are dried and eaten in winter. They are larger than those of our eastern wintergreen but less aromatic.

Twinberry or Honeysuckle, Lonicera involucrata, a shrub of the Sierra Nevada and Cascade Range, has dark purple berries that are eaten by the Indians and considered good by hunters and miners.

EDIBLE NUTS

And close at hand, the basket stood
With nuts from brown October's wood.
—J. G. WHITTIER

IN the number and variety of edible nuts, the Unites States is doubly blest. It is doubtful if any other country, at least in temperate latitudes, can show so many species. The largest group, the hickories, is found on no other continent. Some of our species, by selection, have been greatly improved and now to some extent are cultivated. Others have excellent possibilities. The wood of some of the hickories is the hardest and strongest produced in this country, and that of the black walnut is probably the most valuable.

The majority of our nut-bearing trees and shrubs are native of the East. It would have been a blessing to the Indians had more grown in the West. They have the nut pines (piñons), however, and make great use of them.

The gathering of nuts has always been a pleasing recreation for young people. Probably nothing else has induced so many boys and girls to go to the woods in autumn at the time of the change of leaf, when they are most beautiful. I truly pity the boy or girl who has never had the opportunity and privilege of going nutting.

ROCKY MOUNTAIN NUT PINE, OR PIÑON
Pinus edulis

THIS is a small pine tree inhabiting the dryer mountainous regions from Colorado south and west into Mexico at altitudes of 5,000 to 7,000 feet. It is probably at its best in New Mexico, where it reaches a height of thirty to thirty-five feet in some cases, and a diameter of one to two feet. The trunk is very short, the spreading branches often reaching to the ground. The short stiff leaves are generally two in a group, sometimes three. They are curved, three-fourths of an inch to an inch and a half long. The cones are often a little wider than long, or about an inch and a half high, light brown and glossy. They mature the second season. The scales are few and very thick. The seeds are about half an inch long, nearly as thick as wide, or very slightly flattened, with short wings which remain with the cone when the seeds fall. This pine is a very important source of food of the Indians and Mexicans. Wooton and Standley in their *Flora of New Mexico* say: "Large quantities of the seeds are gathered every year to be eaten. They are very palatable, having a sweet flavor, especially after having been roasted."

The One-Leaved Nut Pine or Piñon, Pinus monophylla, common in the dry mountain regions of Utah, Nevada, Arizona, and

One-Leaved Nut Pine (Pinus monophylla)

California, is a very similar tree growing in like situations, but is easily distinguished by having only one leaf at a place. It sometimes reaches a height of forty feet, is generally spreading and often round-topped. The cones are similar to those of the Rocky Mountain Nut Pine but are larger—two or more inches high and about as wide. They mature the second season. The thick scales are slightly four-angled. The thick seeds are a little more than half an inch long, somewhat pointed. The short narrow wings remain with the cone when the seeds drop.

The seeds of the nut pines are sold by the bushels even in the eastern markets. They are sweet and pleasant and are in great demand. I have watched the Indians gathering them from the One-Leaved Nut Pine in the desert ranges of southern California where they are not only an important food but the chief money crop or article of trade. I have had the Indians roast them for me in their campfires so that I could eat them under various conditions.

The seeds of the nut pines take the place of wheat for the Indians of the southwestern mountains. They often eat them raw or roasted, but as a general thing the nuts are pounded or ground into meal, then baked in cakes or cooked as gruel. In seasons when the pine trees are fruitful, it is claimed that an industrious Indian family can gather fifty bushels in one month. The nut harvest is in autumn before the snow falls.

John Muir thinks that this is the most important tree of the Great Basin region and that the nut pine crop of Nevada, in good years, is greater than the wheat crop of California; but very little of it is gathered.

The seeds of the nut pines are gathered by the pack rat and placed on a pile at the bottom of its conical nest. These nests, often two or three feet high, are built of sticks, stones, pieces of cactus, and anything that the rat can carry that attracts its attention. The pine nuts ripen and fall to the ground in autumn and are stored by the rats apparently for their supply of winter food. The Indians tear the nests apart and frequently get a quart or more of piñon nuts from each nest. In the scattered woodlands east of Santa Fe, New Mexico, where both the Rocky Mountain Nut Pines and pack rats are quite abundant, I found nearly every rat's nest pulled apart or turned over for the pine nuts.

The Parry Pine, or Four-Leaved Pine, Pinus quadrifolia, is another nut pine that grows in the semidesert region of southern California and Lower California. The nuts and cones are almost exactly like those of the one-leaved species, but the tree is distinguished by having four leaves to the fascicle.

When food is scarce, the seeds of some of the other western pines, especially the Digger Pine, Pinus sabiniana, are gathered and eaten by the Indians. When hard pressed for food, they also make use of the inner bark of two or three species of pines. The Shore or Scrub Pine, Pinus contorta, which grows along the coast from Alaska to northern California, is one of these. Julia E. Rogers says of this species:

The Indians cut the trees down and strip out the inner bark. This is broken into pieces by the patient squaws who mash it in water into a pulp which they mold into large cakes. Then a hole is dug in the ground and lined with stones, and a fire kindled. When the stones are hot, the embers are removed, and the cakes packed in with leaves of the Western Skunk Cabbage between. A fire of damp moss is built on top, and the baking takes an hour or more. Then the cakes are laid on slat frames and smoked for a week in a close tent. Now they are ready to be put away for future use or to carry in canoes or on ponies to distant places.

This "hard bread" is prepared for use by breaking it in pieces and boiling them until soft. The pieces are skimmed out and laid on the snow to cool. "Ulikou" fat is used on this strange Alaskan bread as we use butter.

BLACK WALNUT

Juglans nigra

THIS stately forest tree ranges from Massachusetts to Minnesota and Nebraska, south to Florida and Texas. It does best in a rich loamy soil and is often seen along fences, roadsides, and the borders of woods. Squirrels and other animals buried the nuts along fences where young trees appear. Of course, it was origi-

Black Walnut (Juglans nigra)

nally a forest tree, common on hillsides and rich bottom lands; but now we rarely see it in the dense woods. The pioneer farmers, in clearing the land, often allowed the Black Walnut to grow in the fields and about their homes, and some were probably planted. In many places this tree is becoming scarce on account of being cut for its valuable wood.

Under favorable conditions, the walnut may reach an extreme height of nearly a hundred feet and a trunk diameter of six feet. In the open, it develops large branches and is wide-spreading. The bark is dark brown with prominent ridges and deep furrows. The large compound leaves are very similar to those of the butternut. The staminate catkins, which appear with the leaves, also resemble those of the butternut. The fruit is nearly round, yellowish green, roughly dotted, an inch and a half to nearly three inches in diameter. The husk does not split open like that of the hickory nut. The nut within is dark, rough, very hard or bony, nearly round, only slightly compressed, and an inch and a quarter to nearly two inches in diameter. The sweet, edible, four-celled kernel has a pleasant but strong taste and is quite oily.

The Black Walnut is one of the most important of our native nut-bearing trees. Large quantities of the nuts are gathered for home use, and many are sold in the markets. The American Indians made great use of them as an article of food. The husk has an aromatic odor and is sometimes used for dyeing and tanning.

The mere name of Black Walnut brings pleasant recollections to the minds of many grown folks who spent their youth in the country. The writer recalls that three quite large trees stood along the fence that enclosed the grounds of the school he attended when a lad. The trees gave us exercise in climbing. When we returned to school in autumn, the nuts on the branches were excellent targets for our marksmanship. They were gathered and carried home by the boys who did not naturally fall heir to such articles of diet. In the adjoining field, a few rods from the fence, stood a great spreading walnut tree, presumably the parent of all the others in the immediate neighborhood. The ground was often nearly covered by the unhulled nuts. The farmer owning the land always left the nuts for the boys. Here during the noon hour of pleasant autumn days, we often congregated to eat walnuts or shuck them to take home. Our fingers were stained a dark brown—the skin almost tanned. With all the washing with soap and water, we could not remove the color and our fingers carried the telltale stains for a week or two. But what a good time we had! Sometimes in the spring we tried the nuts but then after being moist with rain and snow all winter, they were getting ready to grow and had a peculiar sweet taste. I am informed by a friend that even the nuts of the Bitter-Fruited Hickory lose their bitterness, or most of it, after being buried or left out for a winter. I have not verified this by experiment.

The Texas Walnut, Juglans rupestris, which grows along cañons and streams of the Southwest, has small thick-shelled nuts much esteemed by the Mexicans and Indians.

The California Walnut, Juglans californica, is a beautiful tree growing along the west coast. The nuts are small, thin-shelled, and sweet. The Persian or English Walnut, Juglans regia, is grafted on its roots so that it can be grown farther north. Another species, Juglans kindsii, is found about old Indian camp sites in central California.

BUTTERNUT, OR WHITE WALNUT, OR OIL NUT

Juglans cinerea

ALMOST every country boy living within its range is familiar with the Butternut tree. It grows best in a rich loamy soil, often near streams. It may be found from New Brunswick to Delaware, and in mountainous regions south to Georgia and Mississippi, and

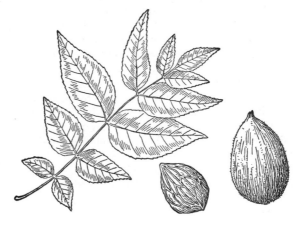

Butternut (Juglans cinerea)

on west to Dakota, Kansas, and Arkansas. It probably reaches its greatest development in the upper Ohio valley and along the Allegheny plateau. In fields and open spaces it rarely grows more than fifty or sixty feet high with a few wide-spreading branches. In woods it often grows tall and more slender. The trunk sometimes reaches a diameter of two or three feet. The bark is light gray with shallow furrows and broad flat ridges. The alternate compound leaves are fifteen to twenty-five inches long. Each leaf is composed of eleven to seventeen leaflets. The leaflets are three to five inches long, sharp-pointed, unequally rounded at the base and with saw-toothed edges. The staminate catkins appear in May when the leaves are about half developed. They are three to five inches long. The pistillate flowers appear in a short spike.

The nuts generally occur in clusters of two to five. They are oblong, blunt-pointed, two or three inches long, and a little more than half as thick. A thin husk covers the outside which, like the young twigs, has numerous sticky hairs and a pungent but not unpleasant odor. The nut itself is ridged and deeply furrowed, the whole surface being very rough. It has four ribs, but they are not prominent. The nut is hard and bony but the kernel is quite easy to separate from the shell. It is sweet and delicious but, like most nuts, is oily. They are much gathered for home use and are often sold in the markets. Some writers state that they soon become rancid. I believe this is only partially true. If kept in a cool dry place, they should be good for nearly a year. When a boy, I lived in the upper Ohio valley, where butternuts and black walnuts were exceptionally abundant. We often gathered large quantities of the former and placed them on the barn floor until thoroughly dry. They were then stored in boxes or barrels and we had no trouble to keep them all through the winter.

The sap of the butternut tree is sweet and is sometimes added to that of the maple for making sugar or syrup. The husks of the nuts and the inner bark contain a rich brown or tan-colored dye which was used by the early settlers; even as late as the Civil War it was used in dyeing the uniforms of some of the regiments.

When soft and green, the young nuts are often pickled. In her splendid book on trees, Julia E. Rogers writes:

The frugal housewife in the country looks with interest upon the butternut when it is half grown—when the pale green, clammy, fuzzy fruit hangs in clusters, surrounded by its umbrella of leaves. If a knitting needle goes through husk and nut without hindrance, it is not too late to make "pickled oil-nuts," which are a delectable relish with meats in winter. The husks and all are put down in vinegar, sugar, and spices. The unpleasant part of this process is the rubbing off of the "fur" after scalding the nuts. This task usually falls to the children.

PECAN NUT
Carya illinoensis
Hicoria Pecan

THE Pecan tree grows to be the largest of all our hickories. It reaches its highest development in the lowlands and river bottoms of the lower Mississippi valley where it sometimes attains a height of one hundred and fifty feet and a trunk diameter of four or five feet. Unlike the other species of the genus, the wood is said to be somewhat brittle.

The bark of the pecan tree is smoother than that of most hickories, but it is moderately rough with furrows and brown ridges.

Pecan Nut (Carya illinoensis)

The buds are small and the scales few. The leaves have eleven to fifteen leaflets which taper gradually, are slightly curved and long-pointed, with saw-tooth edges. As in all the other hickories, the stamens and pistils are in separate blossoms but on the same tree. The staminate catkins are five or six inches long, several in a cluster. The fertile flowers are two to five in a cluster. The fruit is oblong or olive-shaped, the husk thin, splitting in four pieces. The oblong nut is smooth, thin-shelled and pointed. The seeds are delicious—perhaps the best of all our hickories. The pecan is native from southern Indiana, Iowa, and Kansas south to Alabama and Texas. It is planted farther east in the Gulf states.

Large quantities of the nuts are gathered and kept for use or sold in the markets, where they are in great demand, especially in the cities and towns of the North. By selection, many improved varieties have been developed, and large pecan orchards are being planted in the South. If the demand for these nuts increases, their cultivation will prove to be an important horticultural industry.

SHAGBARK OR SHELLBARK HICKORY
Carya ovata
Hicoria ovata

"HICKORY" is an Indian word said to be derived from the name of a liquor made by pounding the kernels and shells of these nuts for a long time in a mortar. After they were finely powdered, water was added and the process continued, until a milky or oily liquor was produced which they called *pawcohiccora*.

The Shellbark Hickory is a large stately tree, often reaching a height of one hundred feet and a diameter of three feet or more. Unless the tree grows in the open, the branches are rather short. The gray bark, which is very hard, has a loose, shaggy appearance, splitting in thin narrow strips or plates which separate from the trunk generally at both ends, but cling tightly at the middle. The light brown wood is heavy, straight-grained, very hard, strong, and elastic, and is much used for ax handles, agricultural implements, etc. It is said to be the best firewood obtainable in America. The leaves have five, rarely seven, leaflets; the two lower ones generally much smaller than the others. The leaflets are sessile except the end one, which has a short stalk.

The staminate catkins are three in a group, each about four inches long. The fruits, nearly round or slightly oblong, vary greatly in size but average about two inches in diameter. The thick husk splits freely into four pieces. The white nuts vary greatly in size and shape. They are generally about an inch long, nearly as wide, slightly compressed, four-angled or ridged and tipped with a point. The shell is hard but quite thin. The kernel is four-celled at the base, two-celled above, large, sweet, pleasant, and slightly aromatic. Because of their color, the nuts are known in some parts of the country as white walnuts. Hale's Paper Shell Hickory nut, said to have been discovered in New Jersey, is an important horticultural variety. Other varieties of this species have been developed.

The shagbark hickory is believed by some to be our most important native nut. Large quantities are gathered and sold in the markets. According to early explorers, the Indians made great use of them for food, gathering them by the bushels. The tree is found in rich soil from New England and southern Canada west to

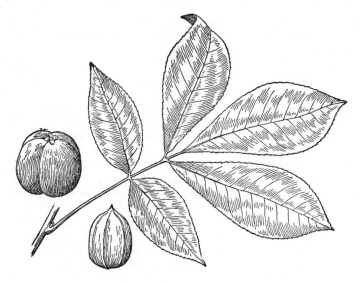

Shagbark Hickory (Carya ovata)

Minnesota and south to Florida and Texas. It probably reaches its finest development in the Ohio valley.

In almost every neighborhood where the Shagbark grows, a few trees are famous for the abundance or the excellent qualities of their nuts. These trees generally grow alone in fields, in the open, or on the borders of woods where their branches reach far out into the sunshine. I have helped to gather a bushel of excellent nuts from one tree. A Shagbark growing in the woods, surrounded by dense forest growth, rarely produces more than enough for the squirrels.

BIG SHELLBARK, OR KING NUT
Carya laciniosa
Hicoria laciniosa

THIS tree in many respects is very similar to the common Shellbark. It is much the same in size and general appearance. The gray bark splits in narrow plates but in general is not so shaggy as in the last species. The heavy straight-grained wood is strong and elastic, and can be put to the same uses as that of the last species. The twigs and buds are orange-yellow—a distinguishing characteristic. The large leaves have seven or nine leaflets, somewhat downy beneath. The staminate flowers are three in a cluster; the pistillate flowers, two to five in a short spike. The fruit is large for a hickory, oblong, slightly ribbed above the middle, two or three inches long. The thick husk is four-valved, sometimes tardily splitting near the base. The large whitish or yellowish nuts are oblong, compressed, pointed at both ends, angled or ridged. The bony shell is thick and hard, the kernel sweet and of fine flavor.

The Big Shellbark grows in rich soil generally in lowlands along streams from New York and Pennsylvania west to Iowa and Kansas, and south to Tennessee and Oklahoma. The nuts are often seen in the markets of our Middle West cities, and are now becoming common in our eastern markets.

Like all hickories, the nuts of this species vary greatly in size and appearance. I have three of these nuts before me as I write, taken from as many different trees. Two of them are of a very light brown color, the third one is an orange-brown. The largest one is more than two inches long and about an inch and a half wide. The smallest one is slightly less than two inches long. I recall a tree of the Big Shagbark that stood on the bank of the Youghiogheny River in western Pennsylvania. At flood time the water was often several feet deep around the tree. The nuts were big (probably two inches long) and shaped much like a large English walnut. The shell was thin and the kernel large and sweet. A pocketful of these nuts supplied trading material for a day at school. Eight or ten nuts were worth a worn-out pen-knife, and three or four would purchase a lead pencil. This was the most famous nut tree for miles around and was probably a hybrid between the Big and the Common Shagbark. It is too bad that it was never propagated. Several other Big Shagbarks grew a quarter of a mile away, but they all bore the large thick-shelled, sharp-pointed nuts.

MOCKERNUT, OR WHITE-HEART HICKORY, OR BULLNUT

Carya alba

Hicoria alba

THE White-Heart Hickory or Mockernut grows to be a large tree, sometimes nearly a hundred feet high, with a trunk diameter of two or three feet. The dark gray bark is close and rough, never shaggy. The trees vary greatly as to appearance: in some the

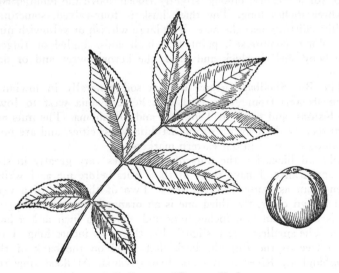

Mockernut (Carya alba)

branches are upright; in others, they may be spreading or slightly drooping. The heartwood is brown; the sapwood, nearly white; and much of the trunk is sapwood, which is heavy, hard, strong, and tough, in great demand for the manufacture of farm machinery. The winter buds, which are slightly downy, are very large, especially the terminal one; hence the name Big-Bud Hickory sometimes applied to this tree. The fragrant leaves have seven or nine leaflets, which are usually widest above the middle and have fine-toothed edges.

The fruit is round or slightly oblong. The husk is thick, four-valved, generally splitting to the base; sometimes the valves are united near the base. The nut is nearly smooth, quite round, slightly angled toward the summit, but little compressed, grayish or brownish, with a very hard shell and a small but sweet kernel.

This hickory grows from eastern Massachusetts to southern Ontario and Nebraska, south to Florida and Texas. It is about the only hickory common to the South Atlantic plain. It reaches its highest development in the middle states, where it thrives best on rich uplands.

My observations lead me to believe that the Mockernut varies more than do our other species. This is especially noticeable in the nuts. They are generally about an inch long, but frequently less and sometimes much longer. I have gathered for comparison many nuts from dozens of trees in different parts of the country and have found the greatest variation. These nuts are sold in the markets, either separately or mixed with other nuts. I recall one tree that stood on our old home farm in western Pennsylvania. The nuts that it bore were large (a few of the nuts still in my possession are each an inch and a half long); the shell, not thick, and the kernel, of excellent quality. Some years we gathered half a bushel of nuts from this tree and enjoyed them.

PIGNUT HICKORY, OR BROOM HICKORY
Carya glabra
Hicoria glabra

In the hardwood forests of western Pennsylvania and the Ohio valley, this is generally the tallest tree, frequently raising its head a few feet higher than its neighbors. In that region, this species seems at its best with a straight trunk often three feet or more in diameter. The gray bark on large trees is close with shallow furrows and narrow ridges. The wood is hard, strong, and elastic, much used for handles and farm machinery. It is so tough that the early settlers used it for making wooden brooms.

The dark green leaves have from five to seven leaflets. The fruit is oval or pear-shaped, slightly compressed, nearly smooth. The husk is thin, splitting only halfway. The nuts are nearly smooth, variable in size but quite constant in shape, generally about an inch long. The shell is sometimes heavy, but usually only of average thickness. The kernel is rather small and sweet or only slightly bitter. Opinions vary concerning the edible qualities of these nuts. One high authority says: "Seeds astringent and bitter, not edible." I have tested the nuts of this species at many places in its range, both east and west, and have yet to find a really bitter nut. Some are slightly astringent and leave a faint bitter taste in the mouth, but they are generally pleasant. We must not confuse this species with the Bitter Hickory, Carya cordiformis, whose seeds are very bitter indeed. Dr. Romeyn B. Hough in his *Handbook of Trees* says of the Pignut, "The nuts are extremely variable in quality, some being quite astringent and others of pleasant flavor." In explaining how this tree probably acquired its name, the author of one of the best tree books tells how the early settlers gathered the shagbarks but left the pignuts on the ground because "the insipid meats were distasteful to human palates—fit only for pigs." Of course, they are not as good as the shellbarks, but the meats are not insipid and can generally be eaten with pleasure. I once sent some nuts of this species to the late Dr. George B. Sudworth, who was then Chief of Dendrology in the Forest Service at Washington, knowing that he was an especially keen student of the hickories, and called his attention to the various opinions concerning their edible qualities. In his reply Dr. Sudworth comments as follows:

What is said about the flesh being bitter is exceptional. The flesh of this fruit is for the most part edible and often quite as sweet as that of *Hicoria ovata* [the Shellbark]. The facts are that large amounts of this nut find their way into market. I have occasionally met with forms of *Hicoria glabra* with fruit that was decidedly bitter; but I think this form is rare.

I have known boys to gather them by the peck when other nuts were scarce and seem to enjoy them.

The Pignut grows in rich soil, generally on uplands, from Maine and southern Ontario west to Minnesota, south to Florida and Texas.

The Small-Fruited Hickory, Carya microcarpa, with bark somewhat shaggy in old trees, is another edible species. It is found from Massachusetts to Michigan, south to Virginia and Missouri. Apparently it is never plentiful enough to be important. The nuts are small, and the seeds very sweet and pleasant.

Other edible hickories have been described from the southern states. It is difficult to give their distinguishing characteristics. The reader need not hesitate if the seeds are sweet.

HAZELNUT, OR FILBERT
Corylus americana

THIS much-branched shrub, common in open thickets, borders of woods, along fences and roadsides, is native from Maine to Saskatchewan, south to Florida and Kansas. It grows in large-spreading clumps, the stems or branches reaching a height of four to seven feet. The young twigs and shoots are brown, densely covered with rough pinkish hairs. This new growth later becomes

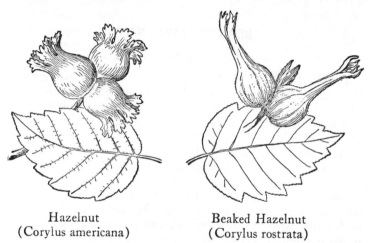

Hazelnut
(Corylus americana)

Beaked Hazelnut
(Corylus rostrata)

smooth. The alternate, simple leaves, on short petioles, are ovate or broadly oval, rounded or heart-shaped at the base, sharp-pointed with toothed edges. It blooms in March or April before the leaves appear. The slender, staminate catkins usually occur singly in the axils of last year's leaves. When mature, they are three or four inches long and move with the wind. The fertile flowers are in scaly buds near the ends of the branches. The nut is partly or nearly enclosed in a downy involucre composed of two leaflike bracts, fringed on the margin. The brown nut, which closely resembles the European filbert, is one-half to three-fourths inch long, sometimes less, about as broad, and slightly compressed. It has a light brown base where it is attached to the involucre; the dark brown part often presents a velvety appearance. The shell is thin, and the seed, sweet.

The nuts are generally ripe in August but remain on the bushes until late in the autumn if not removed by animals. The chipmunk is especially fond of them, and as this little squirrel cannot climb tall trees, the Hazel bush grows at the right height for him. The hazelnut makes up in quality what it lacks in size. It is one of our finest nuts and, if carefully cultivated and selected, might rival the European filbert. It is certainly equal to the latter species in quality.

BEAKED HAZELNUT
Corylus rostrata

THE Beaked Hazelnut is a more northern species, ranging from Nova Scotia to British Columbia, south especially in the mountains to Georgia, Tennessee, Kansas, and Oregon; and a variety of it is found in the mountains of California. It is very similar to the preceding species but a little smaller, growing from three to six feet high. The young twigs and foliage are less hairy. The leaves are narrowly oval, slightly heart-shaped, apex-pointed, irregularly saw-toothed on the margins.

The most striking characteristic of this species is the shape of the two bracts that enclose the nut. They are so united that they form a tubular beak about an inch and a half long with the nut at the bottom. In shape this beak has been compared to a long-necked bottle. The tube is fringed at the end, and the outside is covered with short stiff hairs. The nuts are sweet and pleasant, and in every way are almost exactly like those of the common Hazelnut. I have collected them from Maine and northern New York to southern Pennsylvania, and if any difference, the nuts seem a trifle smaller than those of the common Hazelnut. A friend recently sent me some nuts from the California variety of this species. The tubular husks are similar to those of the eastern form, but the nuts are larger, some measuring three-fourths of an inch in diameter and nearly as high, with a broad, flat base.

When boys and girls go nutting in the autumn, the lowly Hazel bushes by the roadside are apt to be overlooked; but the nuts are well worth gathering. They are not bulky, are easily cracked, and there is but little waste.

AMERICAN BEECH
Fagus grandifolia
Fagus americana, Fagus ferruginea

THE American Beech is a large forest tree with round head and wide-spreading branches, the lower ones generally horizontal or sometimes drooping. The smooth bark is light gray, often blotched. The wood is hard and strong, close-grained, used for planes, shoe lasts, and woodenware. The ovate-oblong leaves are alternate on the twigs. They are nearly twice as long as they are broad, with a tapering base and pointed apex, straight-veined, coarsely toothed, with a papery texture. The petioles are from a quarter-inch to a half-inch long.

The flowers appear when the leaves are about one-third grown. The sterile and fertile blossoms are in separate flower clusters but on the same tree. The staminate flowers are arranged in balls that hang on long stems. The fertile blossoms appear in the axils of the upper leaves and mature into a bur about an inch long, covered with soft recurved prickles. The bur turns brown in autumn, divides into four valves exposing the two brown, triangular nuts or seeds. The nuts are about half an inch long, somewhat concave; and the kernel is small but very sweet and nutritious.

The American Beech grows in rich soil on both high and low lands from Nova Scotia and southern Canada to Minnesota, south to Florida and Texas. The nuts are larger and more numerous in the northern part of its range. The trees generally have to be large before they bear. In the central and southern states often not one tree in a dozen bears nuts. On account of the small kernel, boys and girls rarely take the trouble to gather beechnuts. Squirrels and bluejays are very fond of them. The nuts are sometimes gathered in the North, especially in Canada, and sold in the markets of northern cities.

AMERICAN CHESTNUT, OR SWEET CHESTNUT
Castanea dentata

> And when the chestnut burr
> Broke open with the frosts, its store disclosing,
> The squirrel, wild with joy,
> Disputed with the boy
> His right of thus his winter food disposing.
> —Walter Cooper

This large forest tree is native from Maine to Michigan, south to Georgia and Arkansas. The alternate leaves are oblong lanceolate with acute apex and margins with coarse teeth. The petioles

American Chestnut (Castanea dentata)

are rarely an inch long. The leaves are smooth and somewhat glossy above, lighter beneath.

The chestnut is one of the last trees to bloom, the flowers appearing in the latter part of June or early in July. In the northern part of its range, the blossoms rarely appear before the latter month. The catkins bearing the stamens are light straw-colored, from six inches to nearly a foot long. The bur formed from the pistillate flowers is green, prickly or spiny, from two to three inches in diameter. It turns yellowish brown on ripening, bursts open about the time that the first frost appears, showing the velvet lining and from one to three dark brown glossy nuts. These vary in shape according to the number in a cell. The size and quality also vary greatly, some trees in a neighborhood becoming famous for the large size of the sweet nuts produced.

Under favorable conditions, the chestnut tree reaches a height of nearly a hundred feet and a trunk diameter of six or eight. In the forest, it grows tall but in open fields it develops a round top with long spreading branches. The bark has long flat ridges with straight grooves between them. The wood is quite light but durable when exposed to the weather or in contact with the soil— hence valuable for posts and rails.

The American Chestnut is, or at least was, our most valuable tree. Large quantities of the nuts were formerly gathered for home use, and bushels were shipped to the cities to supply the markets. A fatal fungus disease introduced from abroad has killed nearly all the chestnut trees east of the mountains, and its ravages are now passing far west of them. There seems to be no remedy, and the disease may utterly destroy this valuable species. Sprouts come up from the roots of the dead trees, and we hope disease resistant forms may be developed.

Few if any trees have entered more into the lives of the American people than the chestnut. The pioneer, in clearing the land, often let a few choice trees stand in his fields or about his home where his family could gather the nuts. In the forests, wild turkeys, squirrels, and other animals fattened on them. Every autumn, when a boy, the writer helped to gather chestnuts—often a bushel or more—to nibble at during the winter months. One famous tree stood on the old home farm that was our joy and the envy of the neighbors. The nuts were the largest and sweetest of any chestnuts of this species that I have ever known.

My friend A. L. Rowe, who has written some delightful things about trees, reminiscently tells of the American Chestnut:

If I were permitted to return to childhood for just one time, I think I would select a bright afternoon in October when the chestnut burs had burst asunder, revealing their hidden treasures. Then, with Father, as in days of yore, we would go up through the orchard to the chestnut tree that stood just beyond. I would see him climb that tree and with a long pole knock the showers of nuts from those golden burs; and I, a little boy, would gather them from among the fallen leaves with a joy that only innocent childhood knows.

CHINQUAPIN
Castanea pumila

THE Chinquapin is a small tree with a maximum height of forty feet and a trunk diameter of two feet. It is generally in the form of a spreading shrub ten or twelve feet high. The oblong, alternate leaves, on short petioles, are pointed at each end. They are from three to six inches long, less than half as wide, with straight veins and sharp-pointed teeth. They are dark green and smooth above, and white woolly beneath. The staminate catkins are from three to five inches long. The numerous burs are an inch to an inch and a half in diameter, commonly arranged in a spikelike cluster. The outside is covered with short stiff spines. The Chinquapin blooms in June, and the brown nuts are ripe in September. The burs contain only one nut each, or rarely two. The nuts are round, somewhat pointed at the top, only about half as large as those of the American Chestnut, and have much the appearance of a small acorn. They are very sweet and pleasant to the taste.

The Chinquapin is found in dry woods and thickets from southern New Jersey and Pennsylvania to Indiana and Missouri, south to Florida and Texas. It is sometimes cultivated much farther north.

Another Chinquapin, Castanea nana, grows in the states bordering the Gulf of Mexico. It is a low shrub that by means of underground stems spreads into large clusters. The small burs have few prickles, and the nuts are slightly larger than those of the common Chinquapin.

The Bush Chinquapin, Castanopsis sempervirens, is found through the western mountains. It is a spreading evergreen shrub that often covers large areas. It generally grows at altitudes above five thousand feet and is often found on sunny slopes more than ten thousand feet above the sea. The burs are quite large, and the nuts slightly resemble filberts. I have gathered them in the mountains of southern California, but they are a favorite food of the western ground squirrels, and these frisky creatures take their full share.

The Giant Chinquapin, Castanopsis chrysophylla is a tree of the mountains of northern California and Oregon. This tree may reach a height of one hundred feet with thick rough bark. The leaves are shaped like those of the American Chestnut, but the margins are entire, dark green above, yellow or golden beneath. The burs are quite like those of the American Chestnut, but the nut, less than half an inch long, has quite a hard shell. The kernel is sweet and is much appreciated by the Indians.

WHITE OAK
Quercus alba

SEVERAL species of oaks bear acorns that are somewhat sweet and are sometimes collected and eaten. They were much used by the American Indians, who gathered them in large quantities for winter use. The acorns were ground, making a sort of flour which was often mixed with corn meal and baked in the form of cakes. In the mountains of Mexico, the natives still use acorns in this way. In some places, the Indians roast the acorns, then grind them and use the product as a substitute for coffee. In December 1620, the Pilgrims found baskets of roasted acorns which the Indians had hid in the ground.

The White Oak is probably the best known of all our oaks. It ranges from Maine and southern Canada west to Minnesota, south to Florida and Texas. It is especially abundant on the west slopes of the Appalachian Mountains and in the Ohio valley. It grows to be a large forest tree with rough light gray bark, often deeply furrowed. The obovate leaves have five to nine oblong lobes. The acorns mature the first season. The cup is deep saucer-shaped and rough, about three-fourths inch across. The ovoid acorns, nearly an inch high, ripen and fall in September. They are often gathered and stored by squirrels. I have friends who when camping, have tried the edible qualities of these acorns by grinding them into a coarse meal and mixing it with flour in making griddlecakes. They have pronounced the cakes edible and quite agreeable.

In some species of oaks it takes two seasons to mature the acorns. Among these we may mention the Black Oak, Red Oak, and Pin Oak. Others mature their acorns in one season. The sweet and edible acorns belong to the latter group. Among these we have the following species:

The Western White Oak, Quercus lobata, is a large and beautiful tree of the southwestern United States. Julia E. Rogers in her interesting *Tree Book* writes of the acorns of this species: "The Digger Indians store them for winter use, and depend upon them as the source of their bread. They are roasted and hulled, then ground into a coarse meal, which is made into loaves and baked in rude ovens in the sand."

The Cow or Basket Oak, Quercus Michauxii, found from Delaware to Indiana and Missouri, south to Florida and Texas, bears acorns that are sweet and edible.

The Rock Chestnut Oak, Quercus Prinus, whose bark is so valuable for tannic acid, bears acorns that can be eaten. This tree is found from Maine and southern Ontario south, especially along the mountains, to Alabama and Tennessee.

Yellow or Chestnut Oak, Quercus Muhlenbergii, *Quercus acuminata,* with leaves resembling those of the American Chestnut, is native from Vermont to Minnesota, south to Alabama and Texas. The acorns are smaller than those of the Rock Oak but have a heavier cup. They are quite sweet, and those I have roasted were rather pleasant eating.

The Chinquapin or Scrub Chestnut Oak, Quercus prinoides, with leaves much like those of the Rock Chestnut Oak, rarely grows more than fifteen feet high. The cup covers half of the sweet acorn. This shrub is found on dry sandy or rocky soil from Maine and Minnesota south to Alabama and Texas. It must not be confused with the Bear or Scrub Oak, Quercus ilicifolia, *Quercus nana,* which grows in similar situations and of about the same size, rarely west of the mountains, and bears numerous bitter acorns.

The Swamp White Oak, Quercus bicolor, *Quercus platanoides,* a large forest tree growing in damp soil from Quebec to Georgia, west to Minnesota and Arkansas, bears acorns that can be eaten. They are quite large and, unlike those of other oaks, are attached to long stems. One author says: "The acorns of the swamp white oak are worthy the attention of any hungry man or beast."

The Indians usually ground the acorns of the various species until the mass was in the form of flour or meal. This was placed in water for a day to soak out the tannin and other bitter substances. The water was then drained off and the material was molded in the form of cakes or loaves or mixed with other food. Sometimes the acorns were roasted before they were ground into meal.

EDIBLE SEEDS AND SEED PODS

SEEDS are extremely important in our diet. The cereals—corn, wheat, rice, oats, rye, and barley—along with peas, beans, and lentils furnish the bulk of the world's food supply.

The American Indian made great use of the seeds of various plants, which he could keep long periods without spoiling or freezing. Of these the grass family forms the most important group. All our cereals are grasses except buckwheat. The red man made much use of wild rice and other native grasses, often making long voyages in canoes to collect them. These starchy foods were generally ground into meal for cakes or gruel.

Vetches, and other members of the pea family, were also used for nourishment by the aborigines. Besides starch, they contain much protein, which is necessary for growth and repair of body tissues. The United States is well blessed with members of this family, some of which, like the garden bean (which is believed to be native of America), it might be possible to develop into vegetables.

There are probably many other plants than the ones mentioned whose seeds have been or could be used for nourishment. Some do not have an agreeable taste; others are difficult to collect; but there are nearly always some that could be obtained and used in case of emergency.

INDIAN RICE, OR WILD RICE, OR WATER OATS

Zizania aquatica

Zizania palustris

THIS coarse grass grows to be four to eight feet high with a stem nearly half an inch in diameter at the base. The lance-linear leaves are from one to three feet long and half an inch to an inch and a half wide. The fruiting panicle is from one to two feet long. Its lower branches are generally spreading and contain only staminate blossoms. The pistillate flowers are on the erect upper branches. The slender grain is nearly three-fourths inch long, round and almost black, falling soon after ripening. The seed is starchy and, when well cooked, is excellent eating. Sometimes the wild rice can be purchased in the markets, especially along the northern border of the United States and in Canada. It commands a good price. We have cooked it in the same manner as cultivated rice (*Oryza sativa*) and served it warm with butter and salt to season or cold with sugar and cream, and can testify that it is pleasant eating. It is claimed that some of the early settlers made much use of it. This cereal was highly appreciated by the Indians, who gathered it for winter use.

Wild rice is found in swamps and along the borders of streams in shallow water from New Brunswick to Manitoba, south to Florida and Texas. In many marshy places, in autumn, it forms the chief food of wild geese, ducks, and other birds that collect among the reeds. Such lands are favorite resorts of the hunter.

The importance of wild rice to the Indians of the North can scarcely be overestimated. It could be kept and used when animal and other vegetable food was scarce or difficult to obtain. Henry R. Schoolcraft called it a precious gift of Nature to the natives. A request for some of this American grain came from abroad. Schoolcraft collected some in northern Michigan or across the straits in Canada, about 1823, and sent it to Europe so that it could be planted along the streams and lakes on the other side of the Atlantic.

Wild rice
(Zizania aquatica)

Wild rice grows in great fields around the shores of lakes and along rivers in Minnesota, Wisconsin, Michigan, southern Canada, and elsewhere. The numerous place names of rivers, lakes, and other physical features referring to this native grain indicate its abundance and importance.

The Indian method of collecting it is interesting. One woman slowly paddled a canoe along the rice beds, while another with a stick in each hand bent the stalks over with one hand and struck them with the other, knocking the grain off into the canoe. It was then taken ashore and dried in the sun or sometimes over a fire and then placed in a hole in the ground lined with the skin of an animal, and threshed by tramping with feet or with sticks. It was winnowed in birchbark trays and stored in bark boxes, or in bags made of skins or of cloth. The Indians of that section still resort to wild rice.

GREEN AMARANTH, OR REDROOT
Amaranthus retroflexus
DESCRIBED under Salad Plants and Potherbs.

AMERICAN LOTUS, OR WATER CHINQUAPIN, OR AMERICAN NELUMBO, OR WATER BEANS
Nelumbo lutea

> Resplendent in beauty, the lotus
> Lifted her golden crown above the heads of the boatmen.
> —LONGFELLOW, *Evangeline*

THIS giant water plant ranges from Massachusetts to Minnesota, south to Florida and Texas, but it is quite rare in nearly all sections of its range. It grows in lakes, ponds, and slow-moving streams. The large horizontal tuberous rootstocks are from two to five feet below the surface of the water, or probably below the frost line. The leaves are all from the roots on thick petioles two to five feet long. The leaves are from one to two feet broad, nearly round, somewhat cup-shaped, or edges higher than the middle. They are attached to the petioles near the center. Some float on the surface, but many are held high above the water. The large pale yellow blossoms are held far above the water by thick stems, which are sometimes six or seven feet long and like the petioles have air canals running through them. The flowers are four to ten inches in diameter, with numerous petals and stamens. This magnificent wild flower opens its blossoms in July and August. It is followed by a nearly hemispherical flat-topped fruit or receptacle. The seeds are imbedded in pits in this hardened receptacle. I have a dried one before me that measures exactly four inches in diameter and has twenty-three seed cavities. When ripe, the seeds are dark brown, nearly round, about half an inch in diameter, with a sharp, hard point at the top. They much resemble an acorn and are often called duck acorns. The shell is hard, but the starchy contents are edible. I have tried them both roasted and boiled. Roasting should be done when the seeds are fresh. The seeds dry so hard that they cannot be eaten roasted, and they do not absorb enough water in boiling to become soft unless the process is continued for a very long time. If the shell is first cracked, then they quickly swell up when boiled and become soft. They are very pleasant eating, tasting much like boiled chestnuts but not quite so sweet. These seeds were highly prized by the Indians, who probably introduced the plant east of the mountains. It is said that the entire plant is edible, especially the large starchy tuberous roots, which sometimes weigh half a pound and have a sweet-potato flavor. Fortunately for the plant, is grows deep in the water where it is difficult to reach. It is doubtful if America has a more beautiful and stately wild flower, and it should be protected where possible; but we think it well to record its edible qualities.

The Indian Pond Lily, Nymphaea polysepala, a large yellow-flowered species of the water lily family, is a native of the quiet ponds in the mountain regions of the Pacific Coast states. The Klamath Indians of Oregon collect the seeds, which they call *wokas,* roast them, and eat them as we do popcorn, which they much resemble in taste. They also grind the roasted seeds into meal, which is baked into bread or used for porridge.

BLACK MUSTARD

Brassica nigra

Sinapis nigra

THIS annual plant grows from three to six feet high, erect with rather widely spreading branches. The stem and branches generally have rough hairs, sometimes are nearly smooth. The lower leaves have slender petioles, the upper ones are nearly sessile. The lower ones are deeply cut with a large terminal lobe and a few small lateral ones, all finely toothed around the edges. The upper leaves are oblong and entire. The bright yellow flowers are about one-third inch across. As in all the other members of the mustard family, there are four petals and six stamens. The latter are in two sets—four long and two short. The pods are somewhat four-sided, about half an inch long, appressed against the stem in a long narrow raceme. The seeds are small, dark brown, with a very sharp, pungent taste. The plants mature the seeds in the summer.

Black Mustard (Brassica nigra)

The Black Mustard is found about dooryards, neglected gardens, roadsides, fields, and waste places generally. It is a native of Europe and Asia but has become so thoroughly naturalized in America that it now grows over much of southern Canada and nearly all of the United States. I have found it about mining camps and summer resorts far up in our western mountains. It is the chief mustard used in condiments so often associated with frankfurters. It also has a medicinal use in "mustard plasters." The White Mustard, Brassica alba, with its larger light brown seeds is also used as a condiment, but it is less peppery.

In Europe and Asia, the Black Mustard is frequently cultivated for its young leaves, which are used as a salad and pot herb. It is rarely cultivated in America, but foreign people especially, make use of the young wild plants. The seeds of the black mustard may be ground fine, mixed with flour and a little water and vinegar, and the condiment is complete. The seeds of other mustard plants such as the Peppergrass, Lepidium, may be used as a substitute. In southern California, I found the Santa Rosa Indians mixing the seeds of a Hedge Mustard, Sisymbrium canescens, with their corn meal to make it more agreeable. Seeds that they gave me have much the size, color, shape, and flavor of those of the common Hedge Mustard, Sisymbrium officinale, of the East.

MESQUITE, OR HONEYPOD
Prosopis glandulosa

This is a small tree, often a mere shrub, found in the dry or desert regions from Kansas to Nevada, south to Texas, New Mexico, Arizona, and California and adjacent Mexico. The roots go down for moisture often to a depth of sixty feet. When in tree form, the bark is slightly ridged with reddish brown scales. The twigs are yellowish green with spines in the axils of the leaves. The latter are compound with numerous entire narrow leaflets. The small fragrant greenish yellow flowers appear from May to July. They are arranged in dense axillary spikes from two to five inches long. The bean-shaped pods, when mature, are slightly flattened, nearly straight, and about six inches long. The pulp surrounding the seeds is sweet, hence the name of "Honeypod." The flowers furnish the bees with much nectar for the making of honey. The pods are often eaten by Indians and Mexicans. Prof. E. L. Greene says that the mesquite meal, which the Indians and Mexicans make by drying and grinding the pods and their contents, is perhaps the most nutritious breadstuff in use among any people. The green pods are also gathered by the Indians and, when cooked, are considered a great delicacy.

The Arizona Mesquite, Prosopis velutina, may be only a variety

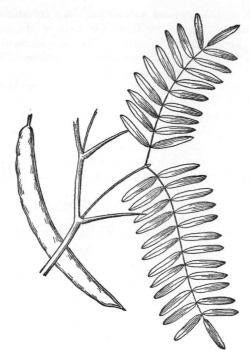

Mesquite (Prosopis glandulosa)

of the above species, but it gradually grows a little larger **with** rougher bark. Its edible qualities are the same.

TORNILLO, OR SCREW BEAN

Strombocarpa pubescens

Prosopis pubescens

THE Screw Bean is a small tree or shrub growing on the desert, especially along watercourses, from Texas to California. In general appearance it is much like the common Mesquite; but the branches are more upright, and the leaves have only five to eight pairs of leaflets. The small greenish white flowers in spikes are also very similar to those of the Mesquite. The sessile pods occur in elongated clusters. They are about two inches long and are in the form of tightly twisted cylinders. They are slightly woody without, somewhat pulpy within. These pods are sweet when chewed, as they contain much sugar. They are pounded into meal and baked into cakes and are an important article of food, especially for the Indians in parts of Arizona.

I have collected the ripe seed pods of both the Mesquite and the Screw Bean in various places throughout their ranges. Those of the latter were apt to be infested with larvae, but the Mesquite pods rarely were. Both make excellent food for cattle and horses when other forage is scarce. A drink is made from the mashed pods of the Mesquite and a crude sort of syrup or molasses is obtained by boiling the sweet pods of the Screw Bean.

LOCUST TREE, OR BLACK LOCUST
Robinia Pseudo-Acacia

THE Locust is a forest tree, now more often found in groves, along fences or the borders of woods. It is native from Pennsylvania to Georgia west to Iowa and Oklahoma. It is planted over a much wider range. It now grows over much of New England and southern Canada, and we find it planted along the highways of California. We recently saw it in bloom the 1st of March along the bayous of Louisiana. It was probably the first native American tree to be planted in England and is said to be more planted there than any other tree of this country.

The Locust may reach a height of eighty feet, and a trunk diameter of three feet or even more. The rough bark is gray on the surface, cinnamon-brown beneath, and rather soft or easily cut. The inner bark is pale yellow—nearly white, with an odor peculiar to this tree. The leaves are compound with nine to seventeen leaflets. The leaflets are an inch to two inches long, oval or oblong, entire, short-stalked. At the base of each leaf is a pair of stipules which are generally spiny. The creamy white flowers are in loose, drooping racemes. They appear in May or early in June and suggest those of the wistaria, their fragrance scenting the air for several rods from the tree. The seed pods are two to four inches long and half an inch broad, rather tardily splitting, often remaining on the tree all winter; they contain from four to twelve seeds each. The wood of the locust tree is hard, strong, very durable in contact with the soil, and makes excellent fuel. The greatest enemy of the tree is the locust borer, which is very common in the East and has practically destroyed many fine groves.

The seeds of the Locust Tree were gathered and cooked by the Indians (with meat, it is said). They are slightly acid and oily and may be used as we use peas and beans. They lose acidity on boiling and become a pleasant nutritious food. The pods could be dried and preserved for winter use when other vegetable food was scarce. Often they are produced in great abundance and hang ۰n the tree until the next spring, thus giving this food a long seasonal range. I have also seen the statement that the pods when young and tender were eaten by the native tribes.

HONEY LOCUST, OR HONEY SHUCKS
Gleditsia triacanthos

THE Honey Locust frequently becomes a large tree, with a height of nearly a hundred feet and a trunk diameter of three or four feet. On small trees, the bark is generally smooth and light or grayish in color. Old trees have rough or deeply cracked or furrowed bark, sometimes covered with small scales. The trunk and limbs usually have stout, branching thorns, often in clusters. These thorns are modified branches and are perhaps the most prominent characteristic of the tree. They are sometimes absent on trees in cultivation. The Honey Locust is wide-spreading with a flat top and nearly horizontal branches. The alternate leaves are once, sometimes twice compound, with numerous leaflets. They give the tree a light, airy appearance. The small greenish or whitish flowers are in short racemes. Sometimes staminate, pistillate, and perfect flowers occur on the same tree; other trees bear a single type—staminate or pistillate. The purplish brown twisted pods are from ten to fifteen inches long and an inch to an inch and a half wide. They are flat, curved, and rather thin, with a sweetish, succulent pulp between the seeds.

The Honey Locust is native from western New York and Pennsylvania south to Florida, and west to Michigan, Kansas, and Texas. It has been naturalized farther east in New England and the middle Atlantic states. It gets its name from the sweet pulp found in the pod between and around the seeds, which is pleasing to the taste and is generally relished by boys. Trees vary as to the quantity and quality of pulp secreted. Sometimes it is slightly astringent. On an island in a large creek near my boyhood home grew a number of native trees of this species where in autumn we boys often resorted to gather the pods, taking many home to nibble at during leisure moments. It is believed that the Indians used the pods and seeds.

St. John's Bread, Ceratonia siliqua, is a tree native of the Mediterranean region from Spain to Palestine. The fleshy pods, eaten both green and dry, were a favorite food of the ancients. They are supposed to have been the "locusts" eaten by John the Baptist. The dried pods are sometimes seen in the city markets of our eastern states.

WILD BEAN, OR BEAN VINE

Phaseolus polystachyus

THIS perennial vine climbs over bushes or trails upon the ground, sometimes reaching a length of twelve to fourteen feet, usually branched. It resembles the common garden bean, with three broadly oval or nearly round leaflets, pointed at the apex. The purple flowers are arranged in long loose clusters. The short-stalked drooping pods are about two inches long, flat and slightly curved. They contain from four to six brown seeds which when ripe are each about one-fourth inch long.

The Wild Bean is found from Connecticut to Nebraska, south to Florida and Texas. It is generally not very abundant; at least I do not come across it often in my walks. The seeds are prepared and cooked like the garden variety and may be used either green or dried. The Wild Bean was highly prized by the North American Indians. In the dried state they could keep it for use in the months when other vegetable foods were scarce.

TEPARY BEAN

Phaseolus acutifolius

AT least eight species of beans are found growing wild from Texas to Arizona, extending into northern Mexico. The seeds or beans of nearly all of them were believed to have been eaten by the Indians, or at least the Tepary was.

This annual plant in some respects is quite like the garden bean; but the leaves are smaller, and the vine more slender. The pods are about three inches long, two-fifths of an inch wide, and somewhat flattened. The bean itself resembles a very small Lima. This plant is found on mountain sides and in the narrow valleys from western Texas to Arizona, and in northern Mexico. Dr. George F. Freeman in *The Standard Cyclopedia of Horticulture* says: "It has been cultivated by the Papago and Pima Indians from prehistoric times and in all probability formed one of the principal foodcrops of that ancient and unknown agricultural race, the ruins of whose cities and irrigating canals are now the only witnesses of their former presence and prosperity."

A cultivated variety of the Tepary Bean was developed by Dr. Freeman which seems suited to the hot dry regions of the Southwest. Either by dry farming or by irrigation larger crops of the Tepary can be raised in that part of the country than can be produced by the garden beans by the same methods.

Dr. Freeman adds: "Well-cooked teparies are light and mealy and have a rich bean-like aroma. Boiled and baked with bacon or mashed and added to soups, they form most acceptable dishes. To such as are fond of the onion, a small amount of this vegetable finely chopped and stirred in during boiling makes a pleasing addition."

GROUND PLUM, OR BUFFALO PEA

Astragalus caryocarpus

Geoprumnon crassicarpum

THIS wild plant, a member of the pea family, is native of the Great Plains from Minnesota to Saskatchewan and south to Missouri and Texas. It is a perennial, branching at the base, and is generally about a foot high, pale green in color. The compound leaves have from fifteen to twenty-five oblong leaflets. The violet-purple flowers are arranged in a short raceme. The plum-shaped pods are each about three-fourths of an inch long, oval, short-pointed, thick, and fleshy. They are spongy or corky when dry and do not split open.

The unripe seed pods, which resemble green plums, are used for food raw or cooked. When cooked, they are usually prepared and served in the same manner as the garden sugar pea where the entire pod is eaten. The plant is often called Buffalo Pea or Buffalo Bean. Sometimes the pods are cooked and spiced for pickles. In parts of Nebraska and in some other states, this wild vegetable food is greatly appreciated. It is claimed that prairie dogs gather the pods and store them up as part of their winter food supply.

In Lewis and Clark's westward journey in 1804, when in the region of South Dakota, they exchanged presents with the Indians. They record among the things received a quantity of a large, rich bean which grew wild and was collected by mice. The Indians

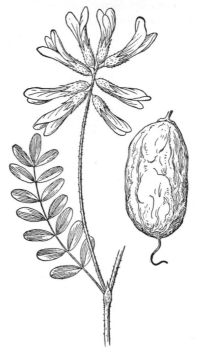

Ground Plum (Astragalus caryocarpus)

hunted for these deposits, collected the beans, and cooked and ate them. The mice referred to were without doubt prairie dogs, then practically unknown, and the bean is the Buffalo Pea.

LARGER GROUND PLUM, OR BUFFALO PEA

Astragalus mexicanus

Geoprumnon mexicanum

THIS is a similar but larger species, with larger fruits than the last. The leaves have from seventeen to thirty-three leaflets. The cream-colored flowers, purple only at the tips, are in short racemes. They are about an inch long, or larger than those of the above species. The fleshy seed pod is nearly round, not pointed, an inch to an inch and a quarter in diameter. The edible qualities of this species are about the same as those of the one described above. The plant has a more southerly range, being found on open plains and prairies from Illinois to Nebraska south to Louisiana and Texas.

UNICORN PLANT, OR DOUBLE-CLAW

Martynia louisiana

Proboscidea louisiana

THIS unique plant is an annual that grows one to three feet high, much-branched, and wide-spreading. The stout stem and branches are covered with soft hairs or down. The leaves are large, sometimes nearly a foot across, broadly oval or nearly round, with a heart-shaped base and blunt or rounded apex. The stout petioles are long as the blade. The flower clusters are arranged in short racemes of several blossoms each. The flowers are an inch and a half to two inches long, nearly as broad, funnel-shaped with five spreading lobes. They are white or pink-purple, generally mottled with yellow or purple within. The fruit is a two-beaked capsule, four to six inches long, strongly curved, woody when mature. The two beaks are longer than the capsule, strong and elastic.

The Unicorn Plant is native from Indiana to Iowa, south and west to Texas and New Mexico but is much cultivated for its fruit, or for ornament, or as a curiosity in the North and East, and has escaped from Maine to western New York and New Jersey, south to Georgia. The fruits when young are soft, tender, and somewhat fleshy, and in that stage are much used for pickles. They reach the pickling stage in summer and early autumn. The plants are sometimes grown in eastern gardens just for "pickling" purposes.

CHIA

Salvia columbariae

THIS sage, one of the best known of all the food plants of the American Indians, grows on the plains, hills, and valleys over much of California and in northern Mexico. It is an annual that begins its growth when the winter rains set in, and reaches a height of six to sixteen inches. There are usually several stalks from the same root, sometimes only one. The dark green leaves are nearly all at the base, deeply cut, rough or hairy. One or two pairs of leaves appear on the stem. The blue flowers, with form characteristic of the mint family, occur in one or two dense whorls. The lobes of the calyx are prickly. Flowers appear from March to May, and the seeds ripen a month or two later.

Chia
(Salvia columbariae)

As the plants are quite low and rigid, the seeds are not easily shaken out by the wind. In places, on the hills and low mountains, on the west side of the Colorado Desert of California, I found this plant abundant. In July, the nearly dead stalks still held the seeds. The Indians take a flat basket in one hand and a stick in the other, and knock the seeds into the basket by beating the dried flower heads. The seeds are cleaned and parched, then ground into meal. The Spanish word *pinole* is used for meal made from seeds of wild plants. Pinole made from Chia is sometimes used alone, forming dark-colored cakes or loaves, but usually it is mixed with wheat flour or corn meal; it gives to the cakes made from this a pleasing nutty flavor. The Indians also mix it with corn meal when making mush or with ground wheat for gruel.

Chia is the Spanish name of this plant, and it is claimed that Cortes found the natives of Mexico using the parched ground seeds for pinole. Even today they are often found in the Spanish markets of the Southwest and in those of Mexico, and Chia seed is an article of trade among the Indians. The dark brown seeds are slightly flattened, and when crushed and moistened are oily and mucilaginous. In the early days of California it was considered that ground Chia seed, moistened, made the "finest poultice for gunshot wounds."

A very popular drink is also made from the seeds of the Chia. For this purpose, the seeds are generally steeped. Sometimes they are crushed or ground, and a quantity of water is poured over the meal; after standing for some time the water is drawn off, and strained. Sometimes it is drunk before the fine particles settle. It is said to be a healthful and nourishing beverage.

The seeds of several other species of wild sage are used for pinole. One of these is the White Sage, Salvia apiana. The seeds of this species are not mucilaginous.

COMMON SUNFLOWER

Helianthus annuus

THE Common Sunflower is a rough annual plant that grows wild from three to six feet high, but in cultivation sometimes ten feet. The alternate petioled leaves, rough on both sides, are ovate, three-nerved, with toothed margins. The lower leaves are generally heart-shaped. The flower heads of the wild plants are from three to six inches in diameter. The brown or dark purple disk is one to two inches broad, surrounded by a row of showy bright yellow ray flowers.

This, the state flower of Kansas, is apparently native from Minnesota to Idaho, south to Texas and California, extending into Mexico. It is said to be also a native of South America. It has long been cultivated, and as a garden plant has flower heads nearly a foot in diameter. It has escaped from cultivation about our eastern cities, where it quickly deteriorates into the wild form.

Although the seeds have long been used as food by the American Indians, the Sunflower is much more appreciated in some countries of Europe than in our own. It is claimed by one of our government authorities that the flowers yield a fine yellow dye that seems permanent, and the bees make a superior quality of honey from them. The seed yields 20 per cent oil which may be used for cooking, burning, or for soapmaking. The oil cake is an excellent food for cattle. Lastly, the stalks when treated like hemp, produce a fine silky fiber.

In Russia the sunflower is much cultivated for the seed, which is of value in feeding all kinds of poultry. It is said that the Russians sometimes get fifty bushels of seed per acre. In that country, the hulled seeds are ground into meal and baked into bread and cakes. In parts of Europe, they are roasted and used as a substitute for coffee. We also find that nearly three hundred years ago the flower buds were boiled and eaten with butter like artichokes.

In Lewis and Clark's Journal, July 17, 1805, when they were along the Missouri River in western Montana, we find the following record:

Along the bottoms, which have a covering of high grass, we observe the sunflower blooming in great abundance. The Indians of the Missouri, more especially those who do not cultivate maize, make great use of the seed of this plant for bread, or in thickening their soup. They first parch and then pound it between two stones, until it is reduced to a fine meal. Sometimes they add a portion of water, and drink it thus diluted; at other times they add a sufficient proportion of marrow-grease to reduce it to the consistency of common dough, and eat it in that manner. This last composition we preferred to all the rest, and thought it at that time a very palatable dish.

ADDITIONAL EDIBLE SEEDS AND SEED VESSELS

WILD or Indian Millet, or Sand Grass, Oryzopsis hymenoides, *Eriocoma cuspidata*. The Wild Millet grows from Iowa to Texas, west to Washington and Lower California. It extends into Canada. It is found on prairies, deserts, and dry hillsides. The Indians made the seeds into flour for cakes or gruel. "The ground seeds were sometimes mixed with cornmeal and made into dumplings."

Wild Oat, Avena fatua, a native of Europe, now found in fields and waste places in the Middle West and especially abundant on the Pacific Coast. The grains resemble those of the common oats but have stiff hairs. The Indians singe these off and then crush the seeds to flour. The common cultivated oats, Avena sativa, has a tendency to go wild in old fields and along roadsides.

Large Rye Grass, Elymus condensatus, grows from Minnesota, Colorado, and New Mexico, west to the Pacific, in damp alkaline soil, reaching a height of six or eight feet. The grains are gathered and made into flour by the Indians.

Wild Wheat, or Squaw Grass, Elymus triticoides, is a more slender grass than the last but grows in similar situations and over much the same range but farther south. The grains are gathered by the Indians and made into meal for cakes and porridge. Other species of Elymus are also used for food by the Indians.

Large Cane, Arundinaria gigantea, *Arundinaria macrosperma,* is the large grass that forms the "canebrakes" from Virginia to Missouri, south to Florida and Louisiana. It grows in river marshes and swamps and is especially common along the Mississippi River. The Large Cane grows from fifteen to twenty-five feet tall, is somewhat woody and branching at the top. Large clusters of seeds are formed at the summit. These starchy seeds were much used by the Indians and early settlers as a substitute for wheat and are said to be nearly as good as that grain. The young shoots are sometimes used as a potherb.

Red Amaranth, or Prince's Feather, Amaranthus hybridus, a weed in waste and cultivated grounds, is found over most of North America. It is cultivated in India for its seeds, which are eaten and used as a potherb in the West Indies. Its seeds are eaten by Indians of the Southwest. See Green Amaranth, in following section.

Prostrate Amaranth, Amaranthus blitoides, which is found as a weed from Maine to North Dakota, south to New Jersey, Missouri, and Kansas, and is native west of the Rocky Mountains. The seeds are gathered by the Indians and made into meal mixed with that from corn, for cakes or gruel.

Goosefoot, or Chenopodium. Seeds of several species of Goosefoots, or Chenopodiums, especially Chenopodium leptophyllum and Chenopodium Fremontii, were gathered by the Indians and parched or ground into meal and used for cakes or gruel.

Saltbush, *Atriplex,* of several species, have starchy seeds used by the Indians.

Islay, Prunus ilicifolia, is an evergreen cherry or plum of California and Arizona. The kernels of the large seeds have long been eaten by the Indians. I have found the kernels bitter and astringent, but this quality is removed by leaching or soaking in hot water.

Wild Lupine, or Wild Pea, Lupinus perennis, ranges from Maine to Minnesota, south to Florida and Louisiana. The seeds are cooked like domestic peas.

Black Medic, or Nonesuch, Medicago lupulina. This clover is widely distributed as a weed over most of the United States. The Indians of southern California greatly relish the seeds.

Vetches, *Vicia sp.* Several species of Vetches were eaten by the Indians. The starchy seeds, which much resemble those of the cultivated pea but are smaller, are often eaten by people of Europe. Some are said to be edible green.

Prairie Bean, Phaseolus retusus, of the western United States, has seeds the size of peas which are said to be very good when well cooked.

Cowpea, or China Bean, or Black-Eyed Bean, Vigna sinensis. Cultivated and escaped from Georgia to Missouri and south. Seeds edible—quite like the common bean.

Blue Flax, or Wild Flax, Linum Lewisii. Found from Wisconsin to Texas west to Alaska and California. Melvin R. Gilmore says in his "Uses of Plants by the Indians of the Missouri River Region": "The seeds of the wild blue flax were gathered and used in cookery both because of their highly nutritive value and for the agreeable flavor which they added to that with which they were cooked."

Chile Tarweed, Madia sativa, is a common plant found about cities and towns and along roadsides on the Pacific Coast. It was probably introduced from Chile. The seeds are sometimes used for pinole. Seeds of some of our native tarweeds could probably serve that purpose.

SALAD PLANTS AND POTHERBS

Herbs, and other country messes,
Which the neat-handed Phillis dresses.
—John Milton

The list of salad plants and potherbs is a large one, yet I have no doubt there are many more that could be used. I have purposely omitted a few belonging to the parsley family (Umbelliferae) because of the danger of mistaking poisonous species of the same family for them.

Most potherbs should not be cooked long or with much water. Some should be parboiled; that is, the water should be changed once or twice to remove a bitter or undesirable flavor. A few with firm tissues require long cooking. A majority of potherbs are rich in vitamins A and C, which are supposed to be partially destroyed by long cooking.

In the springtime, the human body seems to demand green food. This is especially true far out in the country, where fresh vegetables cannot be secured at the markets. The habit of gathering wild green foods for salads and potherbs is much more common in Europe than in America. This is probably due, in part, to the fact that the struggle for existence is always keener in a thickly settled country. This is especially noticeable in China. I find that in our country people from abroad are far more likely to make use of wild foods than the native Americans. It is believed that the reputation of the American people as a bilious race is well founded—a condition due chiefly to their lack of eating enough salads and potherbs.

Half the pleasure of using green foods is in gathering the material—following along hedges, fence rows, or by the brookside, or even into the deep woods. A good observer sees much more than the plants he is hunting, and the time spent in the open air gives one an appetite that makes any food taste better.

IRISH MOSS, OR CARRAGEEN MOSS

Chondrus crispus

THIS marine alga or seaweed is common on the rocky shores of Europe and the east coast of the United States and Canada. It is a variable plant clinging to stones and rocks and is under water most of the time. It often grows in abundance where water is quite deep. It has flat, forked stems or fronds, two to twelve inches long, of a greenish, purplish brown or reddish brown color. It is somewhat cartilaginous and flexible, but when dried becomes brittle. It is gathered at low tide, then thoroughly washed in fresh water and dried. When exposed to sunlight, it bleaches creamy white and is then frequently called "pearl moss" or just "sea moss." After it is thoroughly dried and bleached, it is packed ready for shipment. On the rocky coasts of Maine and Massachusetts, large quantities of it are gathered and prepared for the market. People living along the coast often collect their own supply. It may be gathered at any season.

Irish Moss is used for making soups, blancmange, etc. It is often made into jelly by steeping the plant in boiling water until the jellylike substance is soaked out. It is then strained, sugar and flavoring added, and when cooled, is in the form of jelly. If milk is used instead of water, it forms a custard. When chocolate is added, we have a substance similar to chocolate pudding. When only a small amount of the dried plant is used, it makes a pleasant and healthful drink. Nearly all cookbooks give recipes for the making of Irish Moss jellies and custards.

The name "Carrageen Moss" comes from Ireland, where this seaweed has been in use since the earliest days and is held in high esteem by the peasantry. Other starchy seaweeds are used for food in different parts of the world. The dulse of the English coast is a good example. They all contain iodine, now considered a necessary element of our food.

ICELAND MOSS

Cetraria Islandica

THIS lichen gets its common name from its abundance in Iceland, where it often forms an important part of the food of the inhabitants and is also an article of commerce. It is plentiful in northern countries of Europe and America, especially in the mountains and we include it here because it has been found as far south as New Jersey and Pennsylvania.

Iceland Moss grows from two to four inches high, usually on the ground, but occasionally on rocks. It is a lichen—not a moss—but its erect or leaflike habit gives it somewhat the appearance of a moss. The branches are flat and channeled, but roll in on the margins, forming tubes which end in flattened lobes with fringed edges. It is pale or grayish brown, but when dried and packed, it becomes light gray.

For the table, Iceland Moss is first boiled to remove the bitter taste, then dried and crushed to a powder, after which it is made into cakes or bread, or boiled with milk, forming a jellylike substance. It is said that in seasons of scarcity, the poorer people of Iceland often have but little else to eat. It is palatable and nourishing and is believed to contain about 70 per cent of lichen starch, a substance apparently intermediate between dextrin and starch. One writer states that it contains more starch than potatoes and more flesh-building food than oatmeal. It has long been considered a food and tonic for convalescents and can generally be procured from the drugstores. It is gathered usually in summer and autumn.

ROCK TRIPE, OR BLISTERED ROCK TRIPE

Umbilicaria pustulata

THIS Rock Tripe is a common lichen with ruffly disks one to three inches in diameter, growing on large boulders and rocky ledges, most abundant in the Arctic regions but extending in the Appalachians as far south as North Carolina and Tennessee. I find it most abundant along the eastern ranges of that system. It is leaflike, grayish brown to greenish gray above, light brown beneath, attached to the rock at a point near the middle of the underside. It is somewhat brittle in dry weather but flexible when the weather is damp. Sometimes a white powder develops on the surface. The upper surface of this species has a warty or blistered effect with corresponding pits or indentations below.

Another common species in the eastern United States is Umbilicaria Dillenii. The thallus of this plant is leaflike, smooth, and leathery, brownish green above, black beneath. This is the largest species, sometimes nearly as large as a man's hand. I find this species most abundant along the western ranges of the Appalachian system.

Another species of Rock Tripe with a more northern distribution, but found in the higher mountains of the eastern United States, is Umbilicaria vellea. It is quite similar to the one just described, being quite smooth and leathery, greenish gray with a

Rock Tripe (Umbilicaria)

bloom above, brownish to nearly black beneath. According to Sir John Franklin, this species is more pleasant to eat than the others.

Another Rock Tripe, Umbilicaria Muhlenbergii, extends from the far north into the mountains of the eastern United States. It is large, leathery, sometimes rigid, irregularly pitted, greenish brown above, darker beneath. Franklin states that when boiled with fish roe or other animal matter, it is agreeable and nutritious. It is eaten by the natives of the far north.

Sir John Franklin, Richardson, and other northern explorers lived on a diet of Rock Tripe for weeks, even months, with scarcely any other food. In fact, on one occasion, when Franklin was reduced to starvation in the Arctic regions, Rock Tripe is said to have saved his life. It is often eaten by Canadian hunters and Indians when food is scarce.

I have experimented with three species of Rock Tripe and find them much alike in taste and food value. They are somewhat mucilaginous and, I believe, quite high in nourishment, but they are almost tasteless; at least, the taste is not pleasing. I am quite convinced that they would be much better cooked with meat or other tasty food. I would call it an emergency food.

Ernest Thompson Seton tells us how to prepare Rock Tripe:

First gather and wash it as clear as possible of sand and grit, washing it again and again, snipping off the gritty parts of the roots where it held onto the mother rock. Then roast it slowly in a pan till dry and crisp. Next boil it for one hour and serve it either hot or cold. It looks like thick gumbo soup with short, thick pieces of black and green leaves in it. It tastes a little like tapioca with a slight flavoring of licorice.

BRAKE, OR BRACKEN, OR EAGLE FERN

Pteris aquilina

Pteridium aquilinum

THE common Brake or Bracken is perhaps the most abundant and widely distributed of all our ferns. It is found nearly throughout North America and in Europe and Asia as well. It prefers open situations in woods, pastures, along roadsides and in waste lands generally. In the Sierra Nevada Mountains of California, I have seen acres of it as high as a man's head. In the East it does not grow so luxuriantly but often covers large areas almost to the exclusion of everything else.

The stipe, or stalk, is one to four feet high, erect, stiff when mature, straw-colored or purplish brown. The fronds are one to three feet broad, cut into three widely spreading branches, each of which is again subdivided into sessile leaflets. The upper leaflets are nearly entire above but much indented toward the base.

The lower leaflets are deeply cut. The sori, or fruit dots, are continuous on the under margin.

The bracken is a splendid decorative plant beautifying the woods and roadsides and, unless abundant, should not be used as food. In the spring, just as they are unfolding, the tender stalks and fronds may be gathered and used as a potherb. This is the chief use of the plant in England. The brake is highly prized by the Japanese, who use it chiefly in soups. In the early days in California, vegetables were scarce and the miners gathered the tender fronds of this fern, boiled them, and ate them as asparagus. I have tried this and found the bracken rather pleasant eating. The stalks are somewhat mucilaginous. The Indians of the Pacific Coast often cook and eat the widely creeping rootstocks. It is said that during famine in Europe, the rootstocks are ground and made into bread.

The Sensitive Fern, Onoclea sensibilis, is also used for food. The sterile fronds are taken when ready to unfold and treated like those of the bracken. This is another abundant fern in lowlands from Newfoundland to Saskatchewan, south to the Gulf of Mexico.

CABBAGE TREE, OR CABBAGE PALM, OR PALMETTO
Sabal Palmetto

THE Palmetto is native from North Carolina to southern Florida. It is most abundant in fertile areas called hammocks, especially along rivers and lake shores. A forest of these trees such as we find in places along the St. Johns River in Florida, is really a beautiful sight. Under favorable conditions it grows from forty to sixty feet high with a diameter of nearly two feet. The leafstalks are five or six feet long, and the fanlike leaves are four to six feet long and fully as broad, with narrow deep-cut segments. In spring or early summer, large clusters of white flowers appear which are followed by black drupes, or one-seeded berries, nearly half an inch in diameter. I have watched crows and blue jays feast on the berries, and find that they were used for food by the American Indians.

The large terminal bud of the Palmetto, in its size, shape, and appearance, suggests the head of a cabbage; hence the common name of Cabbage Palm. This bud with the surrounding tissue is considered excellent eating, either cooked or raw. It was eaten by the Indians, and even today, in some sections, the inhabitants make much use of it. In the spring of 1932, in Florida, I saw Palmetto cabbages in the public markets. They are taken at all seasons of the year. It should be used only as an emergency food, for to remove the tender top of a palm always kills the tree. At an isolated area in Florida, I once came across dozens of palmettos dying because their tops had been removed.

SKUNK CABBAGE

Symplocarpus foetidus

Spathyema foetida

WHO ever thought of eating the disagreeable, offensive Skunk Cabbage! I never dreamed of such a thing until one spring when I was camping with friends and a member of the party suggested it. I was the first to condemn it, knowing the fetid odor that accompanies the plant and the charges by some that the root is poisonous. My friend assured me that he had tested the edible qualities of the Skunk Cabbage and found it agreeable and wholesome. In low grounds by the brookside not far from camp, the tender leaves of this plant, all neatly folded and packed, were pushing through the soil, lifting the leaf mold here and there. My friend carefully collected the young leaves with their thick, almost white leafstalks and prepared them for cooking. In the boiling process, he changed the water two or three times. When he had cooked them tender, he seasoned with butter, pepper, and salt. As I said before, I was first to condemn the plant, but now I was first to test its edible qualities and pronounced them good. All the offensiveness had disappeared, and the taste was pleasing.

The Skunk Cabbage is too well known to need description. We are all familiar with its large leaves, often two feet long and a foot wide. It is the first plant to bloom in the spring, sometimes in February pushing up its purplish brown or green-mottled shell-like spathe. Within this is the round fleshy spadix covered with small perfect flowers. Here the bee gets its first pollen.

The Skunk Cabbage grows in moist or swampy ground from Nova Scotia to Minnesota, south to North Carolina and Iowa.

STINGING OR GREAT NETTLE
Urtica dioica

THE very name of nettle suggests something repulsive as an article of diet, yet the Stinging or Great Nettle has long been used for food.

This plant is a native of Europe and Asia but was introduced here and now ranges from Newfoundland west to Minnesota and south to the Carolinas, Missouri, and Colorado. It prefers waste places and roadsides but apparently is never very abundant anywhere.

The Stinging Nettle is a perennial that grows two to four feet high, rather stout, the stem densely covered with stinging hairs. The leaves are ovate, heart-shaped, with sharp but deep teeth. The flower cluster is large, much-branched, forming a panicle. The flowers are very small, greenish, monoecious, that is, staminate and pistillate separate but on the same plant.

The Nettle, so far as I know, is not used for food in America, but it has long been used for that purpose in Europe. In the spring, the young tender tops are often boiled and eaten as greens by the common people of Scotland. According to Sir Walter Scott, it was at one time cultivated in the gardens of Scotland as a potherb. When boiled in soups, it is said to be very palatable. The tender tops are frequently eaten in Belgium, Germany, and other countries of Europe. It is also eaten in northern Persia. I believe it was Oliver Goldsmith who wrote that in olden days a French cook could make seven different dishes out of a Nettle top.

Another species, *Urtica gracilis*, often called Slender Nettle, is taller but more slender than the above described species. It has few stinging hairs, and the leaves are narrower and more rounded at the base. It is a native, covering much the same range as the Great Nettle, but extends west to the Pacific Coast and is common in lowlands. This nettle is also used for food and, taken when young—that is, only a few inches high—is quite tender. It makes a good potherb especially when cooked with other greens. It may be served with melted butter and a little vinegar, or a cream sauce may be used.

There are records of the Wood Nettle, Laportea canadensis, *Urticastrum divaricatum,* having been used as food. This is a plant familiar to many American boys, especially those who have

run barefoot. It is tender and somewhat watery or succulent during most of its growing period. It has a wide range through most
of the United States east of Kansas.

CURLED, NARROW-LEAVED, OR YELLOW DOCK

Rumex crispus

THE Curled Dock is a very common, often troublesome weed
in waste places, pastures, and cultivated fields. It is native of
Europe and Asia but was early introduced into America and is
now found nearly throughout the United States.

It is a smooth, dark green plant, one to three feet tall, with a
deep yellow root. The leaves are nearly all at the base. They are
oblong or lanceolate, six inches to a foot long, generally with a
slightly heart-shaped base. The margins are wavy or curled. The
stem leaves are similar in shape and appearance to those at the
base but only about half the size. The greenish flowers are arranged in whorls in panicled racemes.

The leaves should be gathered in the spring when young and
tender and cooked as a potherb. They should be parboiled or the
water changed by those who do not like the slightly bitter taste.
A little bacon, ham, or salt pork is generally cooked with the dock,
and a small amount of vinegar added. Housewives often prefer
to mix the greens, using dock, dandelions, and the tender tops of
Horse-Radish or Mustard.

The Broad-Leaved or Bitter Dock, Rumex obtusifolius, is also
recommended for greens. It is a native of Europe but is now a
common weed in this country, as far west as the plains. In many
respects it is quite similar to the Curled Dock. It is generally
more robust with broader leaves. It also has a more bitter taste.

Another introduced species is the Patience Dock or Spinach
Dock, Rumex Patientia. It is now quite common in the East and
extends as far west as Kansas. It is a tall, smooth species, generally from three to five feet high, with ovate-oblong or lanceolate
leaves. The leaves are sometimes two feet long. The flower panicle is dense. This plant has long been cultivated in Europe for
early greens. It is sometimes cultivated for that purpose in this
country but seldom gets to the markets. It is considered a good
potherb.

MOUNTAIN OR ALPINE SORREL
Oxyria digyna

THIS member of the buckwheat family is found from Alaska to Greenland and in northern Europe and Asia. In the East it is found as far south as the White Mountains, but in the West it extends through the higher mountains to New Mexico and southern California. It has broad smooth, chiefly basal leaves, and greenish or reddish flowers in a panicle resembling that of a dock. The fleshy or succulent leaves have a pleasing acid taste, and the plant may be used in salads or as a potherb. It often grows about mining camps in the northern mountains.

LAMB'S QUARTER, OR WILD SPINACH
Chenopodium album

THIS coarse weed is a very common annual that grows from two to seven feet tall with a stem slightly grooved and almost woody when mature. Large plants are often much branched. The leaves are rhombic-ovate, or the uppermost lanceolate with angular toothed edges. They are one to four inches long. From their shape the plant is sometimes called Goosefoot. The generic name *Chenopodium* is Greek for Goosefoot. The leaves are generally white mealy beneath. The whole plant often has a pale bluish green color. The minute green flowers are arranged in spiked panicles.

The Lamb's Quarter is a native of Europe and Asia but was early introduced into this country and is now found all over North America except the extreme north. This plant usually grows in cultivated fields. It has an especial liking for potato fields, coming up after cultivation has ceased. On an acre planted in potatoes, I have seen Lamb's Quarter enough to supply a dozen families two or three meals a week. It is probably the most common weed that might be used as human food. When small, six to ten inches high, the plants are succulent and tender, and in that stage are very desirable as a potherb. Many of the Indian tribes of the Southwest gather and cook it as a spinach. I have a friend who much prefers it to the latter plant. In Europe it has long been used as food though rarely cultivated. It should be cooked and served like spinach. In fact, the beet, spinach, and Lamb's Quarter all belong to the same botanical family. It is said to be best when cooked for about twenty minutes and served with butter and a little lemon juice or vinegar. The plants should be gathered in spring and summer when small and tender.

Many of the Indian tribes of the West gather and cook Lamb's Quarter. It is sometimes eaten raw. They also gather the seeds, grind them into meal which is baked in cakes or used in gruel. Part of August and September, 1934, I spent in New Mexico, where I studied the food habits of the Indians. The Lamb's Quarter was growing about almost every pueblo visited, where it was apparently cultivated or at least protected. The natives call it "Quelite." Frémont's Goosefoot Chenopodium Fremontii, a similar plant, was often growing with it.

GOOD-KING-HENRY, OR WILD SPINACH

Chenopodium Bonus-Henricus

THIS is another goosefoot that closely resembles the Lamb's Quarter; but the leaves are not mealy, and the plant grows only from one to two feet tall. It is a perennial, that is, a plant that comes up from the same roots year after year. The leaves are triangular, with the angles quite acute or sharp; the margins are entire or slightly wavy. The lower leaves have long petioles, but those of the upper leaves are short. The small flowers are green, resembling those of the Lamb's Quarter in appearance and arrangement.

The Good-King-Henry is a native of Europe that was introduced into American gardens and later escaped. It may now be found wild from Nova Scotia to Ontario, south to Maryland and Ohio. In this country it is apparently never abundant anywhere. It has long been cultivated in Europe, where it was a favorite with good King Henry. In England it also goes under the names of Mercury and Allgood. Before the introduction of spinach, the broad, succulent leaves were much used as a potherb. One authority says: "Formerly cultivated in English gardens but of late neglected, although certainly of sufficient merit." The young shoots have been used as a substitute for asparagus. This potherb should be prepared, cooked, and served the same as spinach.

The Upright or City Goosefoot, Chenopodium urbicum, and one

or two other species of this genus are also used as a substitute for spinach.

RUSSIAN THISTLE

Salsola kali var. tenuifolia

THE Russian Thistle grows most everywhere, in vacant soil, over the western states on the plains and along the eastern seashore. It is too familiar to need description. One would think that a plant so prickly would be unfit for food, but some housewives in the western states take the young, tender plants when only a few inches high, carefully cut and wash them and boil until tender, then serve with butter. When cream sauce is added it may be served on toast. The supply is inexhaustible but the period when it is edible is rather short. This is the most common "tumbleweed" of the Rocky Mountain and plains states. Plants should be gathered in spring and early summer.

GREASEWOOD

Sarcobatus vermiculatus

THIS shrub is found from the Rocky Mountains to the Pacific in alkaline, clay soil of desert valleys. It usually grows three or four feet high but may reach a height of six or eight feet. The numerous young branches are grayish white; the narrow, fleshy leaves are flattened above, rounded beneath.

The tender twigs of this shrub are sometimes gathered by the housewives of Utah (and probably by those of other western states), carefully washed and cut into short pieces and boiled until tender, then served with butter or cream sauce.

POKE, OR SCOKE, OR PIGEONBERRY

Phytolacca decandra

Phytolacca americana

THE Pokeweed is a stout, strong-smelling perennial that grows from four to eight feet tall. The root is large and poisonous. From it in the springtime several thick succulent erect shoots appear. The stalks which branch and spread near the top vary in color from green to reddish purple. The leaves, which are ovate-lanceolate, are five to ten inches long, pointed, with wavy margins. The flowers and fruits are in racemes, four to seven inches long. The blossoms are greenish white, and the berries when ripe are dark purple, about one-third inch in diameter, filled with a purplish crimson juice which is sometimes used for ink—hence the name Inkberry, which is often applied to this plant.

The Poke is a native from Maine to Minnesota, south to Florida and Texas. It prefers a rich loamy soil in neglected places, along fences, or in uncultivated ground. It especially likes clearings or "new ground."

In the spring, when the young Poke shoots are a few inches high, they are cut off just above the ground and cooked after the manner of asparagus or spinach. Care must be taken not to get any of the root in with the green shoots, for the root is bitter and poisonous. Dr. Frederick V. Coville wrote of the young stems of the Pokeweed:

They are thick and succulent like the stems of asparagus, and are not only used by the country people, but are commonly brought into the city markets where they are sold under the name of "sprouts." In the United States it is not cultivated in the proper sense of the word, although those who bring it into the markets are careful to allow it to maintain itself in the areas in which it becomes established. The French, however, always apt in testing and making use of every kind of food, have introduced the plant into cultivation in Europe.

GREEN AMARANTH, OR REDROOT

Amaranthus retroflexus

The Green Amaranth, often called Pigweed, is naturalized from tropical America and now may be found over the greater part of the United States. It grows as a weed in gardens and cultivated soils, or even in waste lands, reaching a height of three or four feet or even more. The stout stem is little branched, slightly hairy, and somewhat rough. The dull green leaves are ovate, long-pointed, with wavy margins, and the petioles or leaf stems are nearly as long as the leaves. The greenish flowers are in long panicled spikes.

The shiny black seeds of this and other amaranths were formerly used for food by the Indians. They were parched or ground into meal, which was baked in cakes or used for porridge. The leaves

were also used for food. The plant should be taken when young
and tender. Like the Lamb's Quarter it may be found in a young
growing state from spring until autumn. It should be cooked like
spinach and served with butter and vinegar, if the latter is desired.
On account of its mild flavor it may be cooked with stronger-
flavored greens to make it more appetizing. It is claimed that the
Indians of the southwestern states cultivated this plant for its
seeds.

PURSLANE, OR PUSLEY

Portulaca oleracea

THIS fleshy, trailing annual is a native of India, where it was
used for food more than two thousand years ago. Some think that
it may have been native to Persia. It was early introduced into
Europe, where it has been used as a potherb for centuries. During colonial times it was naturalized in America; and it has spread
not only over this country and southern Canada, but over Mexico
and even into South America. It acts like a native in the southwestern United States.

The small alternate leaves are thick and fleshy, spatulate, obtuse, scattered. The light yellow flowers open only on sunny morn-
ings. They are small and last but a few hours. The petals generally number six or seven, and the stamens about eleven.

The purslane is found in almost every old garden in this country.
It especially revels in a fertile sandy soil, and often becomes a
troublesome weed. Charles Dudley Warner calls it "a fat, ground-
clinging, spreading, greasy thing, and the most propagatious plant
I know."

Purslane is cooked and served like spinach. The fleshy stems
are sometimes pickled. In England the young stems and leaves
are often used as a summer salad. In southern Europe it is sometimes used in soups. In China and India it is much used as a
potherb. It has never been much valued in America, but in Europe
several upright cultivated varieties have been developed. As a food
plant it certainly has value. Dr. Coville, botanist of the United
States Department of Agriculture, wrote: "As a potherb it is very
palatable, still retaining, when cooked, a slight acid taste. It can
be heartily recommended to those who have a liking for this kind
of vegetable food." In Mexico it is frequently seen in the markets
where vegetables are sold.

INDIAN LETTUCE, OR SPANISH LETTUCE, OR MINERS' LETTUCE

Montia perfoliata

Claytonia perfoliata

THE Indian Lettuce, a very close relative of the eastern Spring Beauty, is found native from British Columbia and Idaho south to California, Arizona, and northern Mexico. I have found it in abundance at many places in California, where it grows on banks and under trees, preferring a moist situation.

The stem, which is six inches to a foot high, arises from a bunch of basal leaves. These leaves vary greatly in shape. Some are very narrow, others nearly round or even kidney-shaped, on long petioles. More than halfway up the stalk there is a single pair of leaves so united as to form a disk or cup completely encircling the stem. Above this is a raceme of white or sometimes pinkish flowers. There are two sepals and usually five petals. Generally several stems arise from one cluster of basal leaves.

Altogether this is an odd and dainty plant which grows larger and coarser in cultivation. The somewhat fleshy leaves and stems are tender and crisp. The Indians are said to be very fond of it and eat it raw as a salad or cooked as a potherb. In the early gold-mining days of California, it was very difficult to get fresh fruits and vegetables, the lack of which brought on scurvy and other diseases. The miners resorted to this and other plants for greens; therefore the name of Miners' Lettuce. The miners probably learned its use from the Indians or possibly from the Spaniards on

Miners' Lettuce
(Montia perfoliata)

the Pacific Coast. For food, it should be gathered in the spring.

This plant has been introduced into Europe, where it is cultivated under the name of Winter Purslane, and is used for salads or as a potherb. In places in Europe it has escaped as a weed. It also grows wild in Cuba, where it was introduced and has escaped.

COMMON CHICKWEED

Stellaria media

Alsine media

THIS very common weed has been naturalized from Europe and Asia and is found in gardens, fields, waste places, cultivated grounds, or in the woods over most of the United States; in fact, it is now found over most of the world.

The Chickweed is an annual although it frequently lives over winter. In the central United States it probably could be found in bloom every month in the year. The plant is tufted and very much branched. The stems are weak and reclining, sometimes a foot long. The leaves are opposite, ovate, rather sharp-pointed with entire margins. The lower leaves are petioled; the upper ones, sessile. The small white flowers are in terminal leafy clusters or solitary in the axils of the leaves. The five petals are deeply two-cleft.

The Common Chickweed when properly prepared makes a splendid potherb. I have tested its edible qualities and can recommend the plant. It is much used in some parts of Europe. Charles Pierpoint Johnson writes, in *Useful Plants of Great Britain,* "It forms when boiled an excellent green vegetable much resembling spinach in flavor and is very wholesome."

MARSH MARIGOLD, OR AMERICAN COWSLIP

Caltha palustris

THIS is a common wild flower growing in swamps, marshy places, and wet meadows from Newfoundland to South Carolina, west to Saskatchewan and Nebraska. It must be familiar to many people, for more than twenty-five common names have been ap

plied to it. It is one of our most beautiful wild flowers and should
be protected, but its edible qualities should also be a matter of
record.

The Marsh Marigold has a stout, hollow branching stem from
twelve to eighteen inches tall. The basal leaves are on long fleshy
petioles. The blade of the leaf is heart- or kidney-shaped, three
to six inches across. The upper leaves are nearly sessile. The

Marsh Marigold (Caltha palustris)

margins are entire, wavy, or sometimes with rounded teeth. The
flowers appear in April or May. They are bright glossy yellow,
nearly an inch and a half across. There are five to nine petal-like
sepals, which drop early.

In many parts of the country the Marsh Marigold is much
used as a potherb, especially in the spring at or near the flowering
season and before most garden greens are ready for use. It is to
the plant's advantage that it often grows in swampy regions far
out of reach. The leaves and stems are boiled and served in the
same manner as spinach, and many people say that it is the equal
and even superior of the latter plant. In some parts of the country,

the tender flower buds are pickled and used as a substitute for capers.

One housewife gave me the following recipe for creamed cowslips: "Cook the cowslips, add salt, drain well and chop fine. Put a tablespoon of butter into a saucepan, add a tablespoon of flour, and mix thoroughly. Salt and pepper to taste. Add greens and one-half cup of cream or rich milk. Stir until well mixed and you have an appetizing dish ready to serve."

TRUE WATER CRESS

Radicula nasturtium-aquaticum

Sisymbrium nasturtium-aquaticum

THIS familiar plant, naturalized from Europe, thrives best in clear, cold water. It floats, rooting at the nodes, or sometimes creeps. The leaves have from three to nine segments, the terminal one much the largest. The flowers are small and white, in elongated racemes. The pods are half an inch to an inch long.

True Water Cress
(Radicula nasturtium-
aquaticum)

The Water Cress now grows from Nova Scotia to Georgia, west to Idaho and California. In its wild state, it is better known and appreciated by people from foreign countries. The leaves and tender shoots have been used for greens and for salads since ancient times. It is also used as a garnish. Xenophon highly recommended it to the Persians. In western India it is prized by the Mohammedans. The Romans considered it as excellent food for those who had deranged minds. Lord Bacon urged the people of England to use it, but it seems that it was little cultivated in that country before the last century. Now it is much grown and cared for in many parts of Europe. In this country, great quantities are produced for the markets of our larger towns and cities. People who buy it in closely packed bunches generally do not recognize the plant floating in the water. I have seen large patches of Water Cress growing undisturbed in cool running water in unused lands at the very edge of a small city, yet quantities of the plant were brought from a distance to that city's market. It may be gathered at all seasons, but be careful that the water in which it is growing is not polluted.

The Marsh Cress, or Yellow Water Cress, Radicula palustris, is a plant with similar leaves but with upright habit. It has small yellow blossoms and short pods. It is found over much of North America, introduced in the East but apparently native in the West. It grows in wet or marshy places and along watercourses. I find that it is quite a good substitute for the Water Cress. I have seen statements to the effect that it was once cultivated as a salad plant in Europe.

HORSE-RADISH

Radicula Armoracia

Armoracia Armoracia

Cochlearia Armoracia

THE Horse-Radish is a perennial plant introduced here from England, where it was probably naturalized from European countries farther east. In this country it was first planted about dwellings but has since escaped to moist grounds in waste places especially along brooks. In some sections of the East it is reported as a weed. The plants are very persistent, often growing at the same spot years after dwellings have disappeared. My grandfather planted it by his home in western Pennsylvania probably eighty years or more ago, and the clusters still remain after all these years at exactly the same place, having spread but little.

The Horse-Radish has white roots often a foot long and one to two inches in diameter, abruptly branched at the end. A majority of the leaves come from the roots. They are on long, stout, channeled petioles. The leaf blade is nearly a foot long and about half as wide, with wavy edges and spreading teeth. The stem leaves are smaller, sessile, oblong, and toothed. The flower clusters are arranged in panicled racemes. The flowers are small, white, and like all other plants of the mustard family, have four petals. The seed pods, if formed at all, are nearly round. The plants rarely produce seed. The roots may be taken at any season.

The roots have a hot, biting taste and furnish the well known sauce or condiment which is used on roast beef, pork, and oysters. For this purpose, they are grated and mixed with a little vinegar. The use of Horse-Radish is said to be increasing, and as a result, the plant is now often cultivated. The tender leaves in the spring are frequently used for greens and are good for that purpose especially when mixed with dock or other wild plants.

The Horse-Radish has gone under several scientific names in botanical literature; but, strange to say, only one common name is in use, although I have heard country folk refer to it as "Sting Nose."

WINTER CRESS, OR BELLE ISLE CRESS, OR SCURVY GRASS

Barbarea verna

Barbarea praecox

THE Winter Cress is a native of Europe and has been introduced into this country, spreading as a weed in cultivated ground and waste places. It may now be found from Massachusetts and southern New York south to Florida and west to and in the Appalachian Mountains. The glossy green leaves have four to eight pairs of lateral lobes. The flowers, which appear from April to June are yellow, about a quarter of an inch across, arranged in long racemes. As in all plants of the mustard family, each blossom has four petals. The seed pods are one and a half to three inches long, rather sharply four-angled, and are mounted on short, very thick stems or pedicels.

From New York southward, the Winter Cress is often cultivated for use as a potherb or winter salad. In cultivation, especially in the South, it usually goes under the name of Scurvy Grass. As a cultivated crop, the seeds are generally sown broadcast in late summer. In Washington City and elsewhere, in early spring, it is commonly seen in the markets, and in some sections it is highly appreciated. It is grown in gardens in England and is much used in Germany.

Bitter-Cress (Barbarea verna)

The Common Winter Cress or Yellow Rocket, Barbarea vulgaris, *Barbarea Barbarea,* is another European introduction in
general appearance quite similar to the last species. It prefers low
cultivated and waste grounds, and in places is a pest. It has spread
over the eastern and central states but is believed to be native from
Lake Superior north and west to the Pacific Coast. It grows from
one to two feet tall, has glossy green leaves with one to three
lateral lobes and a much larger rounded terminal lobe. The bright
yellow blossoms appear from April to June. The seed pods are
not more than an inch long on rather slender spreading stems or
pedicels. This plant is sometimes used as a salad or potherb and
is probably best mixed with other "greens." It has a bitterness that
to me is not altogether pleasant. This is chiefly removed in cooking by changing the water once or twice. The plant is sometimes
called "Bitter Cress" and is occasionally for sale in the markets
under the name of "Upland Cress." It is said to be also cultivated

in gardens in parts of England and Scotland; and in places on the Continent of Europe it is boiled as kale or spinach.

PENNSYLVANIA BITTER CRESS
Cardamine pennsylvanica

THE Pennsylvania Cress is common along brooks, swamps, and in wet places from Newfoundland to Minnesota and Montana, south to Florida, Tennessee, and Kansas.

This plant is an annual or sometimes a biennial with erect smooth stem eight inches to two feet high, often much branched. The plant has a rosette of leaves at the base with lateral leaves along the stem. The leaves have from seven to eleven leaflets, the terminal one obovate and much larger than the others. The small white flowers are followed by slender seed pods about an inch long when mature. This plant is an excellent substitute for the common Water Cress. It is slightly bitter but not disagreeable. On hikes in the woods. I have often gathered this cress to eat with my sandwiches and have found it a pleasing relish.

Several other plants of this genus have also been used as substitutes for the Water Cress. Among them are the following:

The Cuckoo Flower, or Meadow Cress, Cardamine pratensis, in general appearance quite similar to the Pennsylvania Cress; but the lower leaflets are rounded, and the showy white or rose-colored flowers are half an inch or more broad. It is not abundant but may be found from New Jersey to Minnesota, north to Labrador, also in Europe and Asia.

Round-Leaved, or American, Water Cress, Cardamine rotundifolia, is found in cold springs and brooks from New York to Ohio south to North Carolina and Missouri. It is a weak, often reclining plant with oval or round leaves. It is used as a salad plant, and Asa Gray says of it: "Leaves with just the taste of the English water-cress."

BLACK MUSTARD
Brassica nigra

DESCRIBED under Edible Seeds and Seed Pods.

LETTUCE SAXIFRAGE, OR MOUNTAIN LETTUCE

Saxifraga micranthidifolia

Micranthes micranthidifolia

THE Lettuce Saxifrage is a perennial plant that grows on the borders of cool mountain streams and in swampy places in the Appalachian Mountains from central Pennsylvania south to Georgia and Tennessee. The leaves are in a thick mat at the base of the plant. They are sometimes nearly a foot long, rounded at the top, tapering downward in a margined petiole. The edges of the leaves have short sharp teeth. The flower scape is one to two feet tall, terminating in a loose panicle. The white flowers are nearly a quarter of an inch across. The calyx lobes turn backward. The flowers appear from May to July, followed by sharp-pointed seed pods.

In some of the mountainous sections of southern Pennsylvania, this plant is highly prized by the people. For salads it is probably used more than any other wild plant of the region. They seem to be careful not to destroy the roots, for in places I have found it in abundance along cold mountain brooks. There the natives call it "Deer Tongue," probably from the shape of the leaves. In the springtime, the leaves are carefully gathered and washed, then placed in a stewpan or frying pan where a little bacon or fat salt pork has previously been cut fine and partly cooked. Some sour cream is added, but the cooking is slight—in fact, the leaves are scarcely more than wilted. In that region, garden lettuce is usually prepared and served in the same manner. In most households it is an acceptable dish.

INDIAN RHUBARB

Peltiphyllum peltatum

Saxifraga peltata

WHEN I first saw this plant, which was along a rocky mountain stream in northern California, I immediately thought of the common May Apple or Mandrake of the East. On a nearer approach I saw the plant was larger and coarser. This perennial has a thick fleshy horizontal rootstock from which arises early in the season a naked stem bearing a panicle of white or pale pink flowers. The nearly round or shield-shaped leaves all arise from the base. They are from one to two feet across, slightly cupped or depressed at the center, lobed margin, irregularly toothed. In order to support such large leaves, the plant has thick fleshy petioles or leaf stems, from one to three feet long.

The Indian Rhubarb is found along mountain streams, at elevations of fifteen hundred to nearly six thousand feet, in the Sierra Nevada, Cascade and Coast Ranges, from central California to central Oregon. The thick fleshy leafstalks are peeled and eaten by the Indians, who consider them a delicacy. Sometimes they are cooked after the manner of asparagus. They should be used in spring and summer.

AZALEA OR PINXTER FLOWER

Rhododendron nudiflorum

Azalea nudiflora

THE wild Azalea or Pinxter Flower is one of the most delightful flowering shrubs of the springtime. It is found from Maine to Florida west to Missouri and Texas. An acid soil, especially if it is rocky and sandy, seems to suit it best; hence we often find it growing with the Low-Bush Blueberries and Wintergreen.

The Azalea grows from two to six feet high with alternate leaves, which are generally crowded toward the ends of the branches. These short-petioled leaves, which are bright green above, paler beneath, are two to four inches long, slightly obovate, with toothed margins. The clustered flowers appear in April or May according to the latitude, and open with, or often slightly earlier than, the leaves. The individual blossoms are large, with pistil and stamens that extend much beyond the flower. The pink or nearly white glandular corolla has a very pleasing odor, which has given to the plant the name of Wild Honeysuckle. Early Dutch settlers about New York named this shrub the Pinxter Flower from Pentecost, or Whitsunday, because it blooms near that movable date.

On the leaves or twigs of the Azalea, there often appears an irregular growth an inch or two across. It is quite heavy and solid, crisp and juicy. It may have been made by an insect, but not as a gall. I have cut or dissected many of them and have found no trace of insect life. It is probably an abnormal growth produced or started by bacteria. Some think it may be a modified bud. William Hamilton Gibson, in *Sharp Eyes,* says: "It has no mission in the world except to melt in the mouth of the eager, thirsty small boy. Its cool, translucent, pale green pulp is like balm to his thirsty lips." And again he writes: "How it makes the corners of my jaws ache with thirsty yearning as I think of

Azalea or Pinxter Flower (Rhododendron nudiflorum)

it." These May apples, as they are sometimes called, are excellent for pickling with spiced vinegar and have been used for that purpose since Pilgrim days. By experiment, I find they make a good salad, especially when mixed with other greens. Some years they are quite plentiful, and others they seem scarce. They are usually at their best near the end of May.

COMMON MILKWEED, OR SILKWEED

Asclepias syriaca

Asclepias Cornuti

NEARLY every person is familiar with the Common Milkweed, especially in early autumn when the pods burst and the seeds with their parachute arrangement go sailing off in the wind. However, not so many know that the plant is good as a potherb.

This plant is a native perennial found in old fields, orchards, along roadsides, and in waste places from New Brunswick to Saskatchewan, south to North Carolina and Kansas. It prefers a rich, somewhat sandy soil. It grows from three to five feet tall with a sturdy tough stem. The leaves, in opposite pairs, are oblong, tapering at both ends, from four to eight inches long, nearly half as wide, with short stout petioles. The numerous sweet-

Common Milkweed (Asclepias syriaca)

scented flowers are arranged in globular umbels. The flowers have five sepals, a corolla deeply five-parted, with five upright hoods, each with an incurved horn, and five stamens. The corolla with its hoods is greenish purple or nearly white. The follicle, or warty seed pod, is three to five inches long—when mature, splitting on one side. All parts of the plant contain a milky juice.

For greens, the plants are collected when young and tender— that is, when only a few inches high. Wash them thoroughly, then boil them, changing the water once or twice to remove the milky juice. We have tested this plant several times and find that it needs more cooking than some greens but, when well prepared, is much like spinach. In Canada, the tender stems and tops are prepared and eaten like asparagus. A good brown sugar can be made from the flowers. Frémont found the Indians of the Platte River country eating the young pods, cooking them with buffalo meat. It is also reported that the Indians ate the pods and stems of the Butterfly Weed, Asclepias tuberosa, a common milkweed from the Great Plains east to the Atlantic Coast. This plant has tuberous roots which were also cooked and eaten by the Indians.

CORN SALAD, OR LAMB'S LETTUCE
Valerianella Locusta
Valerianella olitoria

THE Corn Salad is a smooth annual plant that grows from six to twelve inches tall, with forked branches. The basal leaves are spatulate, rounded, or obtuse at the apex. The stem leaves are opposite, sessile, and often toothed; all are tender and somewhat succulent. The small pale blue corolla is nearly regular and funnelform, with only three stamens.

The Corn Salad is a native of Europe, where it is much cultivated as a potherb and salad plant. In some regions of this country it is cultivated; but it has escaped and become naturalized from Maine to Ontario, south to Virginia and Arkansas. It grows in fields and waste places and occasionally along roadsides, and will probably become more abundant as the years go by. It is commonly sold in the markets about New York, where it usually goes by the name of Field Salad. The names Fetticus and Pawnee Lettuce are also used for this plant. As a salad, it is best served with lettuce and Water Cress, with salad dressing, for alone it is rather tasteless. It may be gathered in spring and early summer. It often forms a rosette of leaves in the autumn and may be gathered then.

There are several species of the Corn Salad native of the United States. They have white blossoms but otherwise are so nearly like the European Corn Salad that they are difficult to tell from it, and even more difficult to tell from one another; their most marked difference is in the fruit or seed. They are also collected for salads and to use as spinach. One, the Goosefoot Corn Salad, Valerianella chenopodifolia, is found from western New York to Minnesota, south to Virginia and Kentucky; it generally grows taller than the European species. Another is the Beaked Corn Salad, Valerianella radiata, which grows in low ground from Massachusetts to Minnesota, south to Florida and Texas. Others are native of the Middle West, but all may be used alike.

CHICORY, OR WILD SUCCORY, OR BLUE-SAILORS
Cichorium Intybus

THE Chicory is a native of Europe and Asia but has escaped in North America, where it has become a weed in pasture fields, along roadsides, and in waste lands from Nova Scotia to Minnesota, south to Florida and Kansas, also on the Pacific Coast and locally elsewhere in the South and West. It is a stiff-branching perennial with a deep taproot. It grows from one to three feet tall with rigid angular branches. The leaves are nearly all at the base of the plant, forming a rosette on the ground similar to that of the Dandelion. These leaves are from three to six inches long, spatulate, with cut, lobed, or toothed edges, often curled. The stem leaves are very small and clasping.

The flower heads are sessile, often clustered but generally two at a place; sometimes they occur singly. They are from an inch to an inch and a half across, and of a beautiful blue color, or as Emerson says:

> Grass with green flag half-mast high,
> Succory to match the sky.

From the color of the blossoms, the plant is frequently called Blue-Sailors. Occasionally the flowers are white or pinkish. They generally close by noon, but in cloudy weather may remain open all day.

In the spring, the young leaves of the Chicory, which closely resemble those of the Dandelion, are gathered and boiled as a potherb. The water should be poured off once or twice to remove the bitter taste. They are then served like spinach.

Several cultivated forms of the Chicory have been developed, and in late years it has become a farm crop in some sections. It has often been observed that this plant requires the same climatic conditions as the sugar beet. The tender roots are sometimes boiled and served like carrots and parsnips but they have never become popular. The ground roots are roasted and used as a substitute or adulterant of coffee, or sometimes merely to flavor coffee. Some years, millions of pounds of the root have been imported from Europe for this purpose. As a salad plant, large headlike forms with fine-cut blanched leaves have been developed. Great quantities of this form are sold in the city markets. In New Orleans and some other southern cities, much of the coffee is flavored with Chicory.

DANDELION

Taraxacum officinale

Leontodon Taraxacum

Taraxacum Dens-leonis

THE Dandelion is a plant too common to need description. As a weed it has spread over most of the civilized world. It is a perennial that grows from a long, rather stout root, forming a stemless plant above ground. The leaves grow in a rosette, or basal cluster. They are oblong or spatulate, variously cut and toothed. The edges of the leaves have teeth that are supposed to resemble those of a lion, hence Linnaeus gave it the generic name Leontodon, meaning "lion's tooth." The specific name Dens-leonis means the same thing. Even the common name Dandelion refers to the lionlike teeth of the leaves. The hollow flower stems vary from one inch high on a smoothly cut lawn to fifteen or more inches amid the tall grass. The yellow flowers are in a cluster or head that usually opens only in the sunshine. The blossoms are most abundant in May, but about New York I have found them every month in the year. The plants are much more numerous in the eastern states than they are in the West, and I have never seen them growing wild so robust or in such profusion as along Lake Champlain.

The leaves of the Dandelion are highly prized as a spring green. They are gathered when young and tender, thoroughly cleaned, then boiled. The cooking should not be too long, and those who do not relish the bitter taste had better change the water once or twice. They are generally served with a lump of butter and a dash of vinegar. Many prefer to cook them with a little fat salt pork or bacon chopped fine, then serve with a sour-cream dressing. Some prefer the leaves mixed with other greens. Dandelions are sometimes blanched and used raw as a winter salad. They are often cooked and served cold as a salad with or without vinegar. The

Dandelion (Taraxacum officinale)

dried roots have been used as a substitute for coffee. I also find that the roots have been used as a salad.

This plant has been used as a vegetable since ancient times, yet it has only recently been cultivated. On the vegetable farms of New Jersey I have seen fields or plots of three or four acres planted in Dandelions and cultivated in the same manner as Potatoes. Several horticultural varieties have been developed that form large leafy plants. In spring and early summer, the Dandelion is now a common vegetable in the city markets of New York and vicinity.

WILD OR TALL LETTUCE, OR HORSEWEED

Lactuca canadensis

THE Wild Lettuce is a smooth annual or biennial plant, generally the latter, that grows from four to nine feet tall. The hollow stem has a whitish bloom and is very leafy up to the panicle. The basal leaves are variable, deeply cut, often to the midrib, from five to twelve inches long. The stem leaves are clasping, variously cut and toothed, whitish beneath; the upper ones are often lance-shaped and entire. The flower heads are about half an inch high. The flowers are yellow and numerous, but not many open at one time.

The wild Lettuce prefers a rich, rather moist soil in open places, in hayfields, along fences, open thickets, etc. Horses are very fond of it, hence the name Horseweed. The plant has a wide range, growing from Nova Scotia to British Columbia, south to Georgia, Louisiana, and New Mexico.

When the Wild Lettuce is a few inches tall, up to fifteen inches, the leaves and tender stems make a very good potherb. When boiling, the water should be changed to remove the milk and slight bitter taste, unless the latter is desired. The cooking should not be long continued. A little bacon or other fat meat, cut fine and cooked with the plant, is often preferred. Some add a little vinegar. We have tried the Wild Lettuce and know that it may be used as a substitute for the garden variety, especially as a potherb.

PRICKLY LETTUCE

Lactuca scariola

Lactuca virosa

THIS plant, a native of Europe and well known to the ancients, is now a very familiar weed over much of this country. It is also edible. It grows from two to five feet high. The leaves twist or turn edgewise to the sun; for that reason it is sometimes called Compass Plant. The lower part of the stem and the midrib of the leaves are beset with weak prickles. The leaves clasp the stem with earlike projections. Their margins are sharp-toothed—almost bristle-tipped. The plant is a biennial or sometimes an annual. It frequents fields, waste places, and roadsides and is often a troublesome weed. When a few inches high, it may be cut for salad or a herb. I know of country people who gather it regularly. Some botanists believe that the cultivated lettuce was developed from this species. The Prickly Lettuce is found from coast to coast.

The young leaves are very tender, and for that reason it makes a very good salad plant. Some prefer it cut in pieces with a little chopped onion and served with French dressing. As a potherb, it needs very little cooking and is excellent when served with a hot dressing of melted butter and vinegar. It should be gathered in the spring or early summer.

ADDITIONAL PLANTS WITH EDIBLE STEMS AND LEAVES

I FIND record of the following plants being edible. Most of them I have not tested.

Reindeer Moss, Cladonia rangiferina. This lichen is common on the ground in the northern states and Canada. When crisp it is sometimes eaten by people in Norway. Woodsmen of Canada sometimes drink a strong tea made from it, as a stimulant.

Great American Bulrush, Scirpus validus. This is common in swamps nearly throughout North America. The tender part or base of the stem is eaten fresh and raw by the Indians of the Northwest.

Dayflower, Commelina communis. This and other species of Commelina are now becoming common as weeds in cultivated ground. They are used as potherbs in foreign countries.

Asparagus, Asparagus officinalis. The Asparagus is native of Europe and Asia and was cultivated in Rome before the Christian Era. It escaped from cultivation in America. The first Asparagus that I ever recall having eaten was obtained from plants that grew wild in fence corners along a field. The roasted seeds have been used as a substitute for coffee and are still recommended for that purpose in Europe.

Perfoliate Bellwort, or Wild Oat, Uvularia perfoliata. This bellwort is found from Quebec and Ontario south to Florida and Mississippi. The young shoots are an excellent substitute for Asparagus. The roots are edible when cooked. It should be used only as an emergency food.

True Solomon's-Seal, Polygonatum biflorum. The True Solomon's-Seal is found from New Brunswick to Ontario and Michigan, south to Florida and Tennessee. The tender plant in spring is said to be an excellent vegetable when boiled and served like Asparagus. The American Indians fed upon the starchy root. Francis Parkman states that roots of this plant were used for food by the half-starved French colonists in America.

Trillium, or Wake Robin, Trillium grandiflorum. The Large-Flowered Trillium ranges from Quebec to Minnesota, south to North Carolina and Missouri. According to Kephart, this and other Trilliums "make good greens when cooked." This should be used as an emergency food.

Century Plant, Agave parryi. It is from this and other Century Plants of the Southwest that the Apache Indians prepare their famous mescal, said to be palatable and wholesome. The large budding flower stalk is roasted in stone-lined pits until tender and is then enjoyed by the natives. The Sotols, species of Dasylirion, plants related to the Agaves, are prepared and cooked in the same manner by the Indians.

Slippery Elm, or Red Elm, Ulmus fulva. This forest tree is found from Quebec to North Dakota, south to Florida and Texas. The inner bark is mucilaginous with a sweet and pleasing flavor. When a boy, the writer and his companions chewed it with apparently no ill effects. Trunks of this tree should not be mutilated by removing the bark. To remove it from large roots shows less. The Indians of the Missouri River valley cooked the bark with buffalo fat in rendering out the tallow, to give the latter a pleasing flavor. Emerson, in his *Trees and Shrubs of Massachusetts,* says that flour prepared from the bark by drying and grinding, mixed with milk, like Arrowroot, forms a wholesome and nutritious food for infants and invalids.

Lady's Thumb, or Heartweed, Polygonum Persicaria, *Persicaria Persicaria.* This is a weed introduced from Europe, now found nearly throughout North America, except in the extreme north. Horace Kephart says: "Used as an early salad plant in the southern mountains."

Slender Pigweed, or Spleen Amaranth, or Keerless, Amaranthus hybridus. This annual weed ranges from Canada south to the Tropics. It is a native of tropical America and is much used when young and tender, especially in the South, as a salad plant or potherb. It greatly resembles Spinach.

Palmer's Amaranth, Amaranthus Palmeri. Found in dry soil from Missouri and Kansas, south to Texas, also in eastern Massachusetts. Native of the Southwest. Used as in the last species.

Saltwort, or Glasswort, or Pickle Plant, Salicornia europaea.

Found in salt marshes from Nova Scotia to Georgia, also about salt springs in central New York (where it is much used for pickling) and in salty soil from Manitoba to British Columbia, south to Kansas and Utah, also Europe and Asia. Sometimes used as a potherb in Europe but chiefly used for pickling. Another Glasswort, Salicornia ambigua, which grows in salt marshes along the Pacific coast and also along the Atlantic coast is sometimes used for pickling.

Desert Trumpet, or Pickles, Eriogonum inflatum. This member of the buckwheat family is a common and familiar plant on deserts from California east to Colorado and New Mexico. It grows from one to three feet high, repeatedly forked. The lower internodes are generally much swollen or puffed out. These inflated stems are tender when young and may be eaten raw or used for pickles.

Canaigre, or Wild Rhubarb, or Pie Dock, or Sour Dock, Rumex hymenosepalus. This wild dock, whose roots are used in tanning leather, is native from California to Texas. The stems of the leaves and stalk are crisp and tart and are often cooked as a substitute for Rhubarb, which it quite resembles. It frequently goes under the name of Wild Pieplant. It is best in early spring.

Sea Fig, or Ice Plant, Mesembryanthemum crystallinum, grows wild along the southern California coast. The tender, fleshy stems and leaves have been used as a salad. The Hottentot Fig, Mesembryanthemum edule, native of South Africa, has been introduced on the California coast as a sand-dune binder, and is spreading. It is edible, as the name indicates.

Shepherd's-Purse, Capsella Bursa-pastoris, is found as a weed in fields and waste places nearly all over the world. It has the peppery flavor of other members of the mustard family and was formerly used as a potherb. The Chinese still use the plant. Horace Kephart says: "A good substitute for spinach. Delicious when blanched and served as a salad. Tastes somewhat like cabbage, but is much more delicate."

Peppergrass, Lepidium virginicum. This member of the mustard family is occasionally used as a garnish and sometimes as a salad. It is a weed along roadsides and in waste places.

Penny Cress, Thlaspi arvense. This is another member of the mustard family naturalized from Europe and now found in waste places from Quebec to Minnesota, south to New Jersey and Kansas. It is an edible cress cultivated in places in Europe.

Salad Burnet, or Garden Burnet, or Poterium, Sanguisorba minor, is a native of Europe and Asia and is now naturalized from Maine to New York and Maryland. The young leaves taste like green Cucumbers and are used in salads. It is sometimes cultivated, and several varieties have been developed.

Wild Indigo, Baptisia tinctoria.The young shoots are tender and somewhat resemble Asparagus in appearance. In places in New England, they are gathered and used as a substitute for Asparagus. It is found from Maine to Minnesota, south to Florida and Louisiana.

Red Clover, Trifolium pratense. This and other species of Clover are eaten raw or as a salad by the Indians of California, Arizona, and elsewhere. Probably difficult to digest.

White or True Wood Sorrel, Oxalis Acetosella. Found in cold damp woods from Nova Scotia to Saskatchewan, south to New York and New England and in the mountains to North Carolina; also in Europe and Asia. It has long been cultivated in gardens as a minor vegetable, but never extensively. Leaves acid. Used as a salad and, in parts of Europe, as a spring vegetable.

Violet Wood Sorrel, Oxalis violacea. In woods from Massachusetts to Minnesota, south to Florida and Texas. Its acid leaves are edible. The Yellow Wood Sorrel and also the Sheep or Field Sorrel, Rumex Acetosella, are eaten by children for their pleasing acid flavor. They are sometimes used in salads.

Mallow, or Cheeses, Malva rotundifolia. The Round-Leaved Mallow is native of Europe and Asia and was early introduced into America and now grows in waste lands and cultivated grounds over most of our country. The flat carpels or "cheeses" are edible. The Mallow is cultivated as a potherb in Egypt. Pythagoras thought highly of it as a spinach. Greeks and Romans generally thought well of it. Tender shoots are eaten today as a salad in France and Italy.

High Mallow, Malva sylvestris. Introduced from Europe into United States and Canada. "A wholesome vegetable when boiled." The seeds are eaten by country people.

Whorled or Curled Mallow, Malva verticillata. Introduced from Europe and now found in waste places from Nova Scotia to South Dakota, south to Pennsylvania. "A good potherb" (Kephart).

Early Blue Violet, or Johnny-Jump-Up, Viola palmata. Found from Massachusetts to Minnesota and south, especially along the mountains to Georgia. Porcher says: "The plant is very mucilaginous, and is employed by negroes for thickening soup under the name of 'wild okra.' "

Meadow Beauty, or Deer Grass, Rhexia virginica. Found in

moist, sandy soil from Maine to Florida, west to Iowa, Missouri, and Louisiana. According to Kephart; "The leaves have a sweetish, yet acidulous taste. Make a good addition to a salad, and may be eaten with impunity."

Great Willow Herb, or Fireweed, Epilobium angustifolium, *Chamaenerion angustifolium.* Greenland to Alaska, south to North Carolina, Kansas, and southern California. Generally very common in burned-over lands. Found also in Europe and Asia. The young shoots are used as a substitute for Asparagus. The leaves and young stems when boiled are used as a potherb in Canada and in northern Europe. It is reported that in England the leaves are sometimes used to adulterate tea.

Scarlet Pimpernel, or Poor Man's Weatherglass, Anagallis arvensis. Native of Europe and Asia. Naturalized in this country from Newfoundland to Florida, west to Minnesota and Texas, also on the Pacific Coast. In parts of Asia it is eaten as greens. Used in salads in France and Germany.

Virginia Waterleaf, or Indian Salad, Hydrophyllum virginianum. Quebec to South Carolina, west to South Dakota and Kansas. When young and tender, it is eaten as a salad by the Indians. It is claimed that this plant was eaten by some of the early settlers in this country. Is said to make good greens.

Waterleaf, Hydrophyllum appendiculatum. In woods, New York to North Carolina, west to Minnesota and Kansas. According to Barton, the young shoots are eaten in the spring as a salad (in Kentucky and probably elsewhere) and are highly prized by all who eat them.

American Brooklime, Veronica americana. In brooks and wet places from Quebec to Alaska, south to Pennsylvania, Nebraska, New Mexico, and California. "A salad plant equal to the watercress. Delightful in flavor, healthful, anti-scorbutic." (*Scientific American.*)

Common Plantain, Plantago major. All too common as a weed in North America, Europe, and Asia. Formerly eaten as a potherb in China. Used as a spring green.

Sow Thistle, or Hare's Lettuce, Sonchus oleraceus. A weed in cultivated lands, introduced from Europe. Now found over most of the cultivated regions of the world. Used in Great Britain and Germany as a potherb. Said to be "exceedingly wholesome."

Great Burdock, Arctium Lappa. Introduced as a weed from Europe. The Common Burdock, Arctium minus, is much more common and is found in waste lands over much of the United

States. These despised weeds are said to be cultivated as vegetables in Japan. The large tender leafstalks are peeled and eaten raw, used as a salad, or cooked as Asparagus, which it is said to resemble in flavor. The young flower stalk is cooked in the same manner. The root is also peeled and boiled.

Ostrich Fern, Onoclea Struthiopteris, *Matteuccia Struthiopteris.* The stout scaly rootstocks were cooked, boiled, or roasted and eaten by the Abnaki Indians of northern New England and Quebec. Newfoundland to Virginia, northwest to British Columbia.

Spotted Touch-Me-Not, or Jewel Weed, Impatiens biflora. The succulent stems of the Touch-Me-Not are said to be edible, if taken when the plants are young. It often grows in great abundance. It is found from Nova Scotia to southern Alaska south to Florida, Kansas, and Oregon. Should be used in spring and early summer.

EDIBLE ROOTS AND TUBERS

Where the groundnut trails its vine,
Where the wood-grape's clusters shine.
—JOHN G. WHITTIER

FOR our vegetable diet we depend much upon cultivated root crops such as carrots, parsnips, turnips, and beets, along with the potato, which in reality is an underground stem. I find it is a general belief that the North American Indians got their vegetable food entirely from wild material, especially from roots; but of course this was not the case. They had their cultivated plots or gardens, particularly in the East, where they grew corn, beans, pumpkins, tobacco, and possibly potatoes. They did depend, however, much on wild foods, especially fleshy roots, during certain seasons of the year. This was particularly true in the Far West, where the dry climate made gardening almost impossible. Even to this day, the western Indians make great use of fleshy roots and tubers.

Many roots have an acrid, bitter, or undesirable taste, and frequent changing of the water is necessary to remove this. Sometimes it is removed by boiling, then allowing the roots to dry out thoroughly, after which they may be ground into meal. A majority of our edible roots are perennials that store up food for the future use of the plant. This starchy material may be turned to man's account. Many human beings have starved on the plains and deserts, amid plenty, not knowing what to eat or how to prepare it.

ARROWHEAD, OR ARROWLEAF, OR WAPATOO

Sagittaria latifolia

Sagittaria variabilis

THE Arrowhead is a familiar plant growing in shallow water in ponds and marshes, or along the borders of sluggish streams nearly throughout the United States and southern Canada. It even extends into Mexico. It grows from a few inches to two or three feet tall and varies wonderfully in the form of the leaf. Several other species are very similar, and the earlier botanists of this country did not attempt to separate them. For our purpose we will consider these forms as one species. The rootstock is a tuber with numerous fibrous roots. The leaves are basal on long petioles and vary greatly in size and shape. They are generally arrow-shaped with long-pointed basal lobes. The white flowers are borne on the upper part of the scape, usually in clusters of three. The upper flowers generally bear stamens only, and the lower ones, pistils. The blossoms are an inch to an inch and a half broad; the three sepals persist, but the three rounded showy petals drop after a few days. The seeds, more properly called achenes, are winged on both margins, ending in a curved beak. The flowering season occurs from July to September.

The tuberous roots of the Arrowhead were much used for food by the Indians. They were boiled like potatoes, or sometimes roasted in hot ashes. The Algonquin Indians called the plant Katniss and were very fond of it as an article of food. It was also much used by the Indians of the West, especially those of Oregon, who called it Wapatoo, and where next to the Camas it is said to be the most valuable native food plant. The tubers are eaten by the Chinese in the lower Sacramento valley where this plant is very common and is called Tule Potato. It is claimed that a species of Sagittaria is cultivated in China for its tuberous roots.

Lewis and Clark record how at the mouth of the Multnomah River, now called the Willamette, the native tribes subsisted chiefly on wapatoo, an edible root about the size of a hen's egg and closely resembling a potato. It was their chief vegetable to eat with fish or meat, and an important article of trade.

Near the mouth of the Columbia, they record: "We purchased from the old squaw, for armbands and rings, a few wappatoo roots, on which we subsisted. They are nearly equal in flavor to the Irish potato and afford a very good substitute for bread." All through the winter of 1805–1806, when encamped near the mouth of this river, they continued to trade for wapatoo. It was their chief vegetable food, and was never out of season. On the return journey, Lewis, the botanist of the expedition, observed the Indian women collecting the roots where the Willamette joins the Columbia. The women used a very light, shallow canoe ten to fourteen feet long and two feet wide, that would hold one person and several bushels of roots. He says:

Edible Morel (Morchella esculenta var. conica)

Yucca-Southern Texas, probably Yucca Treculeana

Mandrake or May Apple (Podophyllum peltatum)

Wild or Scarlet Strawberry (Fragaria virginiana)

Blackberry—one of our best edible wild fruits

American Cranberry (Vaccinium macrocarpon)

Photo by George T. Hastings

California Fan Palm (Washingtonia filifera), Palm Canyon, California. Fruit may be seen hanging from the trees

Nest of the pack rat in New Mexico under which is his store of
Nut Pine Seeds

Photo by George T. Hastings

Black Locust (Robinia Pseudo-Acacia)

Palmetto or Cabbage Palm (Sabal Palmetto)

Skunk Cabbage (Symplocarpus foetidus)

Common Poke or Pigeonberry (Phytolacca decandra)

Common Milkweed (Asclepias syriaca)

Arrowhead or Wapatoo (Sagittaria latifolia)

Prairie Apple or Indian Breadroot (Psoralea esculenta)

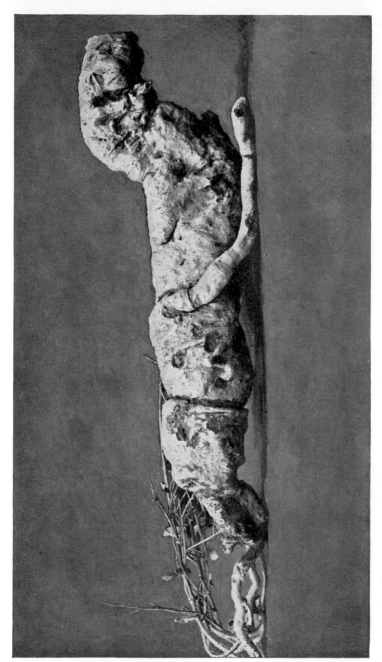

Wild Potato-vine or Mecha-meck (Indian name) (Ipomoea pandurata). This root weighed 15 pounds

Black or Cherry Birch (Betula lenta)
Staminate catkins drooping, pistillate catkins erect

Balsam Fir (Abies balsamea)

Oyster Mushroom (Pleurotus ostreatus)

She takes one of these canoes into a pond where the water is as high as the breast, and by means of her toes, separates from the root this bulb, which on being freed from the mud, rises immediately to the surface of the water and is thrown into the canoe. In this manner, these patient females remain in the water for several hours, even in the depth of winter. This plant is found through the whole extent of the valley in which we now are, but does not grow on the Columbia farther eastward.

CHUFA, OR NUT GRASS, OR EARTH ALMOND

Cyperus esculentus

THE Chufa, or Nut Grass, is an edible plant belonging to the sedge family. It is perennial from tuberous bearing rootstocks. The culms or stems are one to two feet tall, rather stout, triangular. The grass-like leaves which appear near the base have a prominent midrib and are light green, about as long as the stem. At the top of the stalk are three to six smaller leaves forming an involucre around the umbel or flower cluster. The umbel has five to eight rays, which are sometimes compound. The spikelets are numerous, straw-colored, flat, spreading, and many-flowered.

The Nut Grass is found from New Brunswick to Minnesota and Nebraska, south to Florida and Texas; also on the Pacific Coast from California to Alaska, and in Europe, Asia, and many tropical countries. It spreads by the nutlike tubers and sometimes becomes a troublesome weed in low or moist fields.

The tubers, clustered about the base of the plant, are sweet and edible with a nutty flavor. The plant is cultivated, especially in the South and in Europe, for these tubers. We sometimes see them advertised in seed catalogues. We have cultivated the plant and enjoyed eating the tubers. The cultivated form of the plant rarely blooms in the North. It goes under many common names beside those given above, one of which is Edible Galingale.

Another Nut Grass, Cyperus rotundus, sometimes called Coco Grass, is very similar to the species described above. It has fewer rays in the umbel with dark brownish purple spikelets. It is found in sandy fields from Virginia to Kansas, south to Florida and Texas. It is occasionally found in the North, where it was introduced especially about the seaports. It is a bad weed in many places in the South. The nutlike tubers of this plant are also edible.

JACK-IN-THE-PULPIT, OR INDIAN TURNIP
Arisaema triphyllum

FEW if any of our native wild flowers are better known than the Jack-in-the-Pulpit. Even the burning acid nature of the rootstock or bulb has been learned by a great many people in the bitter school of experience. This perennial grows from one to nearly three feet

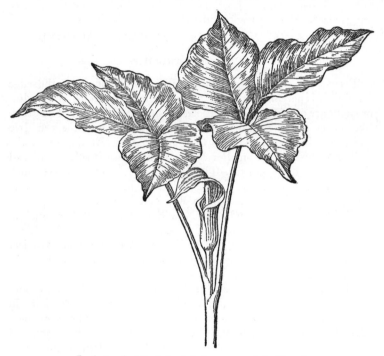

Jack-in-the-Pulpit (Arisaema triphyllum)

high from a starchy bulb or corm. The two petioled leaves are sheathed with the flower stalk; each has three ovate, pointed leaflets, with entire or sometimes lobed margins. The leaves vary greatly in appearance: in some plants, they have a white bloom beneath; in others, the under surface is dark green and glossy. Botanists have described these as separate species, but for our purpose we will consider the various forms as one. At the top of the flower stalk is a round, club-shaped spadix two or three inches long with the small greenish yellow flowers near its base. The lower blossoms are pistillate; the upper, staminate. Surrounding the spadix is a green and purple striped spathe ending in a flap over the top. The colors of the spathe vary greatly and are generally brightest in plants that get the most light. The poet has well described it:

> Fair is the canopy over him seen,
> Pencilled by nature's hand, black, brown, and green.
> Green is his surplice, green are his bands;
> In his queer little pulpit the little priest stands.

The blossoms are followed by a cluster of green berries which become bright red when ripe and are extremely acrid. The bulb, or corm, is slightly flattened or turnip-shaped, with numerous rootlets around the outer edge. It is starchy, but at the same time is the most stinging, burning thing to be found in the woods. It is claimed that the Indians removed the burning taste by boiling, after which these roots were cooked with venison. I have experimented with the Indian Turnip; after boiling and changing the water two or three times, the roots were still too pungent to eat. When I left them for several weeks, or until they were thoroughly dried, the acrid condition naturally left them and the starch became pleasant and nutritious. This would indicate that the burning is produced by physical properties of the bulb instead of chemical properties as is generally supposed. Perhaps it would be best to first boil, then dry them; afterward they could be ground into meal and baked into cakes or used for gruel after the Indian fashion.

The Jack-in-the-Pulpit grows in rich woods, often where it is slightly moist, from Nova Scotia to Florida, west to Minnesota, Kansas, and Louisiana. It may be collected in spring or summer (for experiment).

SWEET FLAG, OR CALAMUS ROOT

Acorus Calamus

THE Sweet Flag, or Calamus, is a close relative of the Indian Turnip, both belonging to the arum family. It grows in masses in swamps, marshy grounds, and along sluggish streams, and is a native of Europe and Asia as well as America. In this country it ranges from Nova Scotia to Minnesota, south to Florida and Texas.

In general appearance, the plant resembles an iris. It has fleshy rootstocks which grow in closely matted masses often many feet in extent, and to the exclusion of all other plants. The sword-shaped leaves resemble those of the iris, but they are glossy and yellow-green while those of the iris are bluish green and dull. The leaves are one to three feet long and about an inch wide with sharp

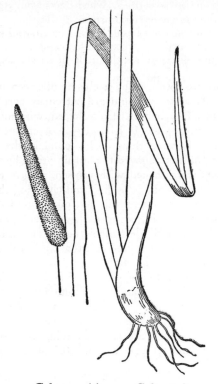

Calamus (Acorus Calamus)

edges and a prominent midvein. They closely sheath each other at the base.

The three-angled scape is nearly as tall as the leaves. About half-way up is the spikelike spadix, standing out at an angle, two or three inches long and about half an inch thick at the base. It is thickly covered with tiny yellowish green flowers. The spadix is not surrounded by a spathe as in most other members of the arum family. The leaflike extension of the stalk is really a spathe. The interior of the stalk is sweet—hence the name Sweet Flag.

The fleshy rootstock has a pungent, biting, aromatic flavor. This furnishes the drug calamus. A little is often eaten raw by the country people as a cure for indigestion. The rootstock is used by confectioners as a candy. To prepare it, they cut it in slices and boil. The pieces are then removed and again boiled in a thick syrup. This forms a candied sweetmeat which, according to Sturtevant, is sometimes sold on the street corners of Boston. I have experimented with it and find that, when properly prepared, it is similar to candied ginger. The pieces should be cut very thin; even then it is apt to be too pungent. The tender base of the stalk is better than the root for flavoring candy.

NODDING WILD ONION

Allium cernuum

FEW people would think that the wild onion belongs to the lily family but that is the case. There are many species of the genus Allium that go under the name of wild onion or wild garlic. All are quite similar in appearance with a bulb at the base, leaves tubular or nearly flat, and flowers in a terminal umbel. All have a strong penetrating odor.

The Nodding Wild Onion grows ten to twenty inches tall from an oblong bulb about half an inch in diameter or less, and nearly three times as high. The bulbs are usually clustered. The leaves, all from the bulb, are very slender, channeled, or nearly flat, generally shorter than the flower stem. The flower scape is bent or nodding at the top, with the bell-shaped blossoms which appear in July or August arranged in an umbel. The petal-like segments of the flower are rose-colored or sometimes white, shorter than the style and slender stamens.

The Nodding Wild Onion is common on banks and hillsides from New York to South Carolina, west to Minnesota, South Dakota, and New Mexico. In the northern part of its range, it goes west to the Pacific Coast.

The bulb of this species is of very strong flavor but, if parboiled, is very good to eat. A little of the leaves or bulb may be used to flavor soups or other eatables where desired. The bulbs are sometimes pickled, and are excellent for that purpose.

Wild onions or garlic are found over nearly the entire United States and southern Canada. Some of the western states have about a dozen species growing within their borders. All may be used alike for food. The Meadow Garlic, Allium canadense, is common from New Brunswick to Florida, west to Minnesota, Colorado and Texas. Its bulbs, like those of the other species, were eaten by the Indians. In places, the bulbs that grow on the top are highly appreciated for pickles. In 1674, when Father Marquette and his men went from Green Bay, Wisconsin, to near the present site of Chicago, their chief food was wild onions, probably this species.

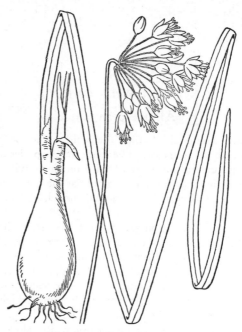

Nodding Wild Onion (Allium cernuum)

The Field Garlic, Allium vineale, naturalized from Europe, is a pest in pasture fields of the eastern states, tainting the flavor of milk and butter. The Wild Leek, Allium tricoccum, is another common species growing in woods.

A western plant, the Swamp Onion, Allium validum, is found from Washington to California. Dr. Harvey M. Hall in his *Yosemite Flora* says of it: "This onion is common in moist places of considerable altitude, the plants often growing in small beds. Although its bulbs are somewhat fibrous they are very acceptable as a flavoring ingredient for soups and stews in a region where vegetables are difficult to procure."

SEGO LILY, OR MARIPOSA LILY, OR STAR TULIP
Calochortus Nuttallii

FEW people realize that the beautiful Mariposa or Sego Lily is good for food, but it is. We must not forget that many wild plants of the lily family (this is one of them) have edible bulbs or corms.

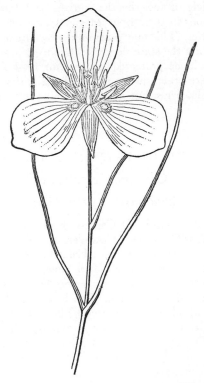

Sego Lily (Calochortus Nuttallii)

The Sego Lily grows from a perennial corm about the size of a walnut. The stem is four to eighteen inches tall, depending much upon climatic conditions. The leaves are few, only two or three inches long, and narrow or grasslike. The plant bears several large flowers on erect stems. The three outer segments or sepals are green with lighter margins. The three wedge-shaped petals are one to one and one-half inches long. They vary in color from white to nearly purple. The base of the petal is yellow with a purplish spot or band above. The three-celled seed pod is about one and one-half inches long when mature.

The Sego Lily is found from Montana to New Mexico, west to California and Oregon. It is most abundant in meadows and on grassy hillsides. The bulbs, or corms, are very palatable and nutritious. They are boiled, roasted, or steamed in pits and are much used as an article of food by the Indians of Utah. It is claimed that the Mormons in their first years in Utah consumed the bulbs in great quantities. This may have influenced the people in making the Mariposa Lily the state flower of Utah. It is a beautiful wild flower and should be protected. Its use for food should be a last resort. There are other species of Mariposa Lilies in the western states with edible corms, but all deserve our protection.

WILD HYACINTH, OR EASTERN CAMASS, OR SQUILLS

Camassia esculenta

Quamasia hyacinthina

OF this and other species of Camass there is much confusion regarding the scientific names. However, the Eastern Camass, or Wild Hyacinth, is one of the most beautiful of our wild flowers, generally blooming in early May. It is a member of the lily family and grows from a coated bulb much resembling a small onion, an inch or an inch and a half high. The leaves are basal, linear, or grasslike, with a ridge on the back. The flower scape is six to eighteen inches tall, with the flowers arranged in the form of a loose raceme. The bracts are slightly longer than the pedicels, or single flower stems. The flowers of six petal-like segments are pale blue or nearly white, about half an inch long.

The Wild Hyacinth is native from western Pennsylvania to Georgia, west to Minnesota and Texas. It grows in rich damp soil in meadows, open woods, and along streams. The bulbs are edible and were much eaten by the American Indians. As a wild flower it should be preserved.

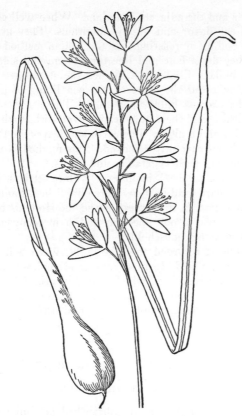

Wild Hyacinth (Camassia esculenta)

CAMASS

Quamasia quamash

THIS is a similar but larger species that grows in the Northwest. It ranges from Montana and Utah west to British Columbia and California. It is a beautiful wild flower growing two feet high with dark blue to almost white blossoms an inch across, in a loose raceme. It grows so abundantly in some places that one writer says the wet meadows look almost like blue lakes. It is claimed that the bulbs form a great part of the vegetable food of the Indians of Vancouver and the adjacent mainland. When well cooked, they are of excellent flavor and highly nutritious. They are generally prepared by boiling or roasting, but the Indian method is probably the best. They dig a hole and line the bottom and sides with flat stones, then build a fire over it. When the stones get thoroughly heated, they rake out the embers, put in a lining of green leaves and place the Camass bulbs upon them. These are covered with more green leaves and the whole heaped over with earth and left to steam for a day and a night. The earth and leaves are then scraped off, and the bulbs carefully removed. This method is used by the Indians in cooking both vegetables and meats.

According to Charles F. Saunders, "White settlers, in the days before their orchards and gardens were established, found in Camas a welcome addition to their meagre and monotonous bill of fare, and Camas pie was a not uncommon dish in many an old time Oregon or California household."

We also find it recorded that the bulbs, when boiled in water until this is evaporated, form a very good molasses used by the Indians on festive occasions, which is highly prized by them. The bulbs of the Camass should be gathered in spring and summer; but, like the Onion to which the plant is related, they may be kept for weeks.

INDIAN CUCUMBER ROOT

Medeola virginiana

THE Indian Cucumber is an unbranched perennial that grows from one to two feet tall. When it first appears in the spring, it is well provided with loose wool which soon drops or disappears. Just above the middle of the stem there is a whorl of five to nine sessile leaves which are three or four inches long, about an inch wide, broadest in the middle, pointed at both ends. In young plants or those that do not bear flowers, these leaves stand at the top like an open umbrella. The flowering plants have another whorl of three leaves (rarely four or five) at the top. These leaves are smaller than the others, only one or two inches long and about half as wide. They are short-petioled or sometimes sessile. From the upper leaves springs a sessile umbel of three to eight greenish yellow flowers which are recurved or bent down. The blossoms are about half an inch across with six petal-like segments. There are six reddish brown stamens and three long threadlike styles. The entire flower suggests a spider. The fruit is a dark purple, three-celled pulpy berry about a third of an inch in diameter on erect pedicels.

The Indian Cucumber has a white, thick tuberous rootstock, two or three inches long, half an inch or more thick. It is brittle and much resembles the Cucumber in taste and smell. The Indians are said to have relished it. In camping or tramping through the woods where they were abundant, I have often gathered two or three to eat with my meal and always found them very agreeable. Where not plentiful this plant should be protected. It grows in rich damp woods from Nova Scotia to Minnesota, south to Florida and Tennessee.

WILD GINGER, OR ASARABACCA
Asarum canadense

THE Wild Ginger is a familiar plant, one of the best known of all our wild flowers. From a creeping, branching, aromatic root-stock, two leaves appear in early spring. These leaves are kidney-shaped or broadly heart-shaped, three to six inches wide, short-pointed at the apex, with a deep and broad sinus or heart-shaped base. The stout petioles are four to ten inches long. The blades and petioles are generally covered with soft hairs forming a velvet-like surface. The rather large flower (there is but one to each plant) appears in May on a short, nodding stem from between the bases of the leafstalks, which is at or near the surface of the ground. The blossom is an inch or more wide with three long-pointed spread-ing lobes. It is brownish purple without, creamy within, and persists until the seeds have ripened. The flowers vary greatly in the shape of the lobes, and chiefly from this characteristic separate species or varieties have been described.

The Wild Ginger grows in rich soil in woodlands from New Brunswick to North Carolina and west to Manitoba and Kansas. An evergreen species is found from Virginia and West Virginia south.

The rootstock of the Wild Ginger has a strong aromatic flavor. A very little is generally enough. It was once used as a remedy for whooping-cough. In Canada the dried rootstocks are used as a spice, and at one time in this country they were commonly used as a substitute for ginger. For this purpose they were dried and pulverized. I have tried to candy the rootstocks of Wild Ginger, after the manner of that of Calamus, with partial success. The taste is

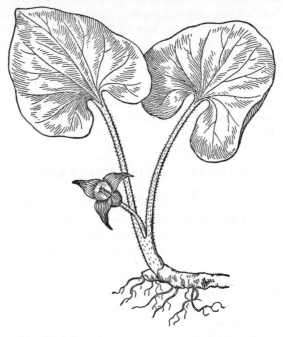

Wild Ginger (Asarum canadense)

much like that of the ginger of commerce. The rootstocks may be collected at any time during spring and summer.

BITTER ROOT, OR SPATLUM (INDIAN)

Lewisia rediviva

ANOTHER edible wild plant of the West is the Bitter Root, a member of the purslane family. It is native from Montana, Wyoming, and Utah west to the Pacific. Probably because of its importance to the American Indian and to the early settlers, as well as from the beauty of its blossoms, it was made the state flower of Montana. The high range of mountains between Montana and Idaho received its name from this plant. Its generic name Lewisia was given in honor of Captain Meriwether Lewis, coleader of the Lewis and Clark Expedition.

The Bitter Root is a stemless perennial with a rosette of spatulate or narrowly oblong leaves growing at the top of a fleshy, carrot-shaped root. The leaves are only about an inch long, somewhat fleshy. The flowers are solitary at the ends of short stems that rise only a little above the leaves. The blossoms are an inch to two inches across, wheel-shaped with eight to fifteen white or pinkish petals, opening in the sunshine. The sepals are generally four to eight, persistent. The plant has wonderful tenacity of life. After being uprooted and dried for weeks or even months, it has the power of reviving when placed in water or in the ground, putting forth leaves and flowers. Its specific name refers to this ability to return to vigor.

Bitter Root
(Lewisia rediviva)

The root of this plant is intensely bitter when raw, but this property is chiefly removed when cooked. It is white, starchy, and without doubt nutritious. The Indians are said to gather it in the springtime when the outer covering or bark, which contains most of the bitterness, slips off easily. This was an important food plant among the western Indians, possibly often from necessity rather than choice.

TOOTHWORTS, OR PEPPER-ROOTS, OR CRINKLE-ROOTS
Dentaria

THE toothworts, or pepper-roots, are familiar wild plants belonging to the mustard family. Two species are common, but others are found in the South and West. The name "toothwort" comes from scales or teeth on the long fleshy rootstock. The generic name is derived from the same thing. The name "pepper-root" of course comes from the peppery mustard flavor of the root.

The Cut-Leaved Toothwort or Pepper-Root, Dentaria laciniata, grows in moist rich woods and along streams from Quebec to Florida, west to Minnesota and Louisiana. The rootstock is deep and jointed with somewhat of a necklace appearance, the joints separating freely. The stem is eight to twelve inches high with the three petioled leaves in a whorl. The leaves are deeply cut in three linear segments; therefore the name Crow's-Foot, sometimes applied to this plant. The divisions of the leaves are toothed or lobed. The four-petaled flowers are white or pink-purple, from a half to

Cut-Leaved Toothwort (Dentaria laciniata)

three-fourths of an inch across. The slender seed pods are about an inch long, somewhat flattened.

The Two-Leaved Toothwort, Dentaria diphylla, has a rootstock just beneath the surface of the ground. It is long and continuous, often branched, sometimes a foot long. It is toothed, but the common name of Crinkleroot is well applied to either species. The leaves are two in number, opposite or nearly so. They are generally a little larger, of a lighter green, with shorter petioles than those of the three-leaved species described above. They are divided into three leaflets with toothed margins. The flowers are white,

about half an inch long. The Two-Leaved Pepper-Root is found
in rich damp woods from Nova Scotia to South Carolina, west to
Kentucky and Minnesota.

Both species of toothworts have edible rootstocks, which are crisp
or brittle with much the taste of Water Cress. The mustard flavor

Two-Leaved Toothwort (Dentaria diphylla)

makes them desirable as a relish. They frequently grow in large
patches of hundreds of plants, and the roots of one or two are sufficient to eat with a meal. Often in eating my lunch of sandwiches
in the woods, I have taken up a root of the toothwort to eat with
it. This can generally be done without destroying the plant. I believe it was John Burroughs who with his companions often gathered
some of the pepper-root on their way to school to eat with their
lunch, but found it so tempting that he frequently nibbled it before
the recess period.

HORSE-RADISH
Radicula Armoracia
DESCRIBED under Salad Plants and Potherbs.

PRAIRIE APPLE, OR INDIAN BREADROOT
Psoralea esculenta

OUT in the prairie states there is a plant whose root was very important to the American Indians of that region. This is the Prairie Apple, or Indian Breadroot. Like other plants used by the early settlers and explorers, it has gone under many different names. Among those not given above are Prairie Turnip or Wild Turnip, Tipsin (Indian), Prairie Potato, Pomme Blanche, and Pomme de Prairie.

This plant belongs to the pea family and is a perennial with a large tuberous or turnip-shaped starchy root, or occasionally a cluster of roots. The stalk is erect, six to fifteen inches high, generally with a few branches. The stems are clothed with soft whitish hairs. The leaves are composed of five obovate leaflets tapering toward the base. They are one to two inches long and less than half as wide, with entire margins. The purplish blue flowers are arranged in short dense spikes. The blossoms, shaped quite like those of a pea, are a little less than half an inch long, surrounded by bracts and calyx lobes nearly as long as the flower. The pods, which are not more than a quarter of an inch long, are enclosed in the calyx tube.

The Prairie Apple grows on prairies and high plains from Manitoba, Wisconsin, and Texas west to the Rocky Mountains. The root is both starchy and glutinous, of an agreeable flavor, and makes an excellent food. It was a favorite diet of the plains Indians, especially of the Sioux. It was often peeled and eaten raw, but generally it was boiled or roasted in the campfire. The roots are entirely beneath the surface of the soil, and the tops mature and break off early, rolling over the prairie like tumbleweeds; therefore the Indians had to gather the roots for winter use in June and July. They were peeled and braided in long strings and hung up in the tents to dry. The Prairie Apple not only was eaten by the Indians but was important to the white adventurers who explored the Great Plains in the early days. It is recorded that John Colter of Lewis and Clark's expedition escaped from the Indians and lived a week on Breadroot tubers. It is also stated that the Indian women found a regular sale for them to white settlers and travelers. It is believed that it would do well in cultivation in the prairie states. If so it would be a wholesome and nutritious vegetable.

Another edible plant belonging to this genus is the Small Indian Breadroot, Psoralea hypogaea. It is quite similar to the above species but smaller with a short round root which in flavor and texture is quite similar to that of the Prairie Apple. Its habitat is the plains region from Nebraska to Texas, west into the Rocky Mountains.

George Catlin, the American author and painter, who lived among the Indians from 1832 to 1839, wrote when camping with the red men in Montana: "The Indians have in store great quantities of dried squashes and dried *pommes blanches,* a kind of turnip which grows in great abundance in these regions. These are pounded into a sort of meal, and cooked with dried meat and corn."

See note under Buffalo Berry.

GROUNDNUT, OR WILD BEAN, OR BOG POTATO

Apios tuberosa

Glycine Apios

Apios Apios

THIS perennial plant is a smooth slender vine, five to ten feet long, climbing over bushes, ferns, and sedges, in low or damp soil, often along the borders of ponds or marshes. In its root system are one to a dozen tubers connected by narrow fibrous strands. These tender tubers are round or somewhat elongated, one to three inches in diameter. The compound leaves have five to seven ovate leaflets, each one to three inches long, sharp-pointed, but rounded at the base. The numerous brownish purple flowers are in axillary racemes. The individual blossoms are about half an inch across, odorous, shaped like those of a pea or bean. There are ten stamens, one of which stands apart from the other nine. The pods are nearly straight, pointed, about three inches long, and much resemble those of a slender bean.

The Groundnut is a twining vine with milky juice and of course is a member of the pea family. It has a wide range, growing in thickets and damp places from New Brunswick to Florida, and on west to Minnesota, Kansas, and Texas. The tubers are sweet and edible. They may be eaten raw, but in my opinion are much better boiled or roasted. I have eaten the groundnut with enjoyment and personally prefer it to the cultivated potato. It is without doubt one of our very best wild foods. It is said to be grown in the flower gardens of France and I have seen it advertised in the florists' catalogues of this country. It seems to be better known in New England

Groundnut (Apios tuberosa)

than in other parts of the United States. It was there that the poet Whittier as a barefoot boy secured that knowledge never learned of schools:

> Where the freshest berries grow,
> Where the groundnut trails its vine,
> Where the wood-grape's clusters shine.

Some of that knowledge was probably handed down by the Pilgrim fathers, for, according to Winslow, during that first hard winter the Pilgrims "were forced to live on ground-nuts." They formed an important food of the American Indians. During colonial days, the Swedes on the Delaware ate them for want of bread. If we did not have the potato, we should probably be cultivating the Groundnut for food. The great botanist Asa Gray once gave his opinion that if civilization had started in America instead of in the old world, this would have been the first edible tuber to be developed and cultivated.

HOG PEANUT, OR WILD PEANUT
Amphicarpa monoica
Falcata comosa

The Hog Peanut is a delicate, slender vine, three to eight feet long, growing in rich woodlands, sometimes along roadsides and fences. It is a perennial that trails on the ground or twines and climbs over low shrubbery. It is generally branched at the base but is simple or sparingly branched above. The stem is often clothed

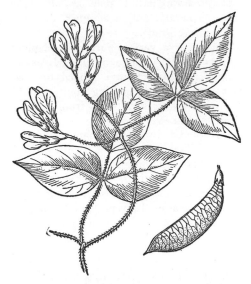

Hog Peanut (Amphicarpa monoica)

with brownish hairs. The leaves have three leaflets half an inch to two inches long, broadly ovate, sharp-pointed, with rounded bases. The flowers, which appear from July to September, are in small loose clusters in the axils of the leaves. They vary from white to pale purple and are about half an inch long and rather showy. The seed pod is only about an inch long, flattened, shaped much like that of a small bean. Down near the roots of the plant on threadlike creeping branches appear tiny blossoms without petals. These flowers are self-fertile and produce pods that develop one big light brown seed in each about the size and shape of a peanut. They are more agreeable than a raw peanut, in fact are very pleasant eating. These large seeds are often quite abundant and appear beneath the dead leaves, generally just under the surface of the ground. They can be gathered without destroying the plant. Hogs running in the woods often root up the leaves and soil in search of them, hence the common name of Hog Peanut. According to Porcher, this plant was once cultivated in the South for its peanutlike fruit or seed.

The Hog Peanut is a common plant from New Brunswick to Florida, west to Manitoba, Nebraska, and Louisiana. A larger form found chiefly west of the Allegheny Mountains has been described as Amphicarpa Pitcheri. It may be only a robust form of the above species. Generally only a botanist can separate the two species as the forms intergrade.

The Hog Peanut was a very important food plant among the American Indians, especially those of the Missouri valley. The women in autumn and early winter robbed the nests of white-footed mice and other rodents, securing "big piles of them." The Dakota Nations when taking these seeds from the nests of animals left corn or other food in exchange.

Father De Smet, the Christian missionary to the tribes of the upper Missouri, says: "The earth pea and bean are also delicious and nourishing roots found commonly in low and alluvial lands. The above-named roots form a considerable portion of the sustenance of these Indians during winter. They seek them in the places where the mice and other little animals, in particular, the ground squirrel, have piled them up in heaps."

BISCUITROOT, OR INDIAN BISCUIT, OR COWAS

Lomatium geyeri

IN the journals kept by Lewis and Clark 1804–1806, we find frequent reference to edible roots obtained from the Indians. One of these found in Idaho and Washington was referred to as Cowas or sometimes just Cows. We now know it as the Biscuitroot of the Indians, a plant closely related to the cultivated Parsnip. In fact, there are several species much alike in appearance. One is Lomatium geveri, another Lomatium farinosum. The genus formerly was called Peucedanum. The small, yellow or white flowers are in compound umbels. They are rather low perennial plants arising from fleshy roots. The leaves are few, rather small, compound or deeply cut. The plants grow in meadows or on hillsides and are frequently abundant.

The Biscuitroot is sometimes eaten raw, when it is said to have a celerylike flavor. Usually it is peeled, dried, then mashed or ground into a sort of flour and made into cakes. The cakes are said to have the taste of stale biscuits; hence by the white people the plant was generally called Biscuitroot. The Indians sometimes made the cakes large enough to be strapped on the saddle and carried for miles on horseback and used when desired.

On their return journey Lewis and Clark recorded, while they were encamped in Idaho in the early summer of 1806:

After a cold, rainy night, during a greater part of which we lay in the water, the weather became fair; we then sent some men to a village above us, on the opposite side, to purchase some roots. They carried with them for this purpose a small collection of awls, knitting-pins, and armbands, with which they obtained several bushels of the root of cows, and some bread of the same material.

The root of this plant was one of the chief articles of trade among the Indians. Again they tell us that with some brass buttons cut from their uniforms and basilicon (an ointment made of black pitch, white wax, resin, and olive oil) and a few small tin boxes, on the second day of June, 1806, two men were sent out to trade with the Indians. They returned with three bushels of edible roots and some Cowas bread. Probably the first entry in the journal concerning this wild food is where they traded for a few large cakes of half-cured bread, made of a root resembling the sweet potato. A little later they say that most of the Indians are on the plains for the purpose of collecting Quamash and Cows, which here grow in great abundance. We described the Quamash elsewhere. From the above citations we see how important the Biscuitroot, or Cowas, was to the natives of the Northwest. It is still used among many Indian tribes of that region.

IPO, OR YAMPA, OR SQUAWROOT

Carum gairdneri

THE Ipo, or Yampa, closely related to the commercial Caraway, is generally considered the finest food plant of the northwestern Indians. It is found from British Columbia to southern California, east to the Black Hills, Colorado, and New Mexico. It usually grows on plains and meadows but sometimes on hills. Lowlands are sometimes whitened by the blossoms, suggesting the Wild Carrot of the East. The plant has a single stem with but few leaves, which are pinnate with three to seven very narrow leaflets. The upper leaves are small and undivided. The white flowers are in compound umbels quite like those of the Wild Carrot. The fleshy roots are single or in clusters.

Squawroot
(Carum gairdneri)

Travelers and settlers in the West and Northwest in pioneer days made much use of this wild food, and its sweet nutty flavor appealed to the Indians. They exchanged it, or traded it to the white settlers for flour or meal. John C. Frémont, who ate it as a vegetable with wild duck, declared it to be the finest of all Indian foods.

The Indians in spring and early summer took the fleshy roots from the ground and washed them; they were placed in water, and the brown skin was removed by tramping with the bare feet. They were again washed and cooked as a vegetable and served with venison or other meat. Sometimes the roots were dried and then ground into flour and baked in cakes. The white settlers treated the roots much as we do parsnips or potatoes and pronounced them fine eating when seasoned with butter. Since the Indian has adopted the white man's method of producing his food, the Yampa is but little used. Some who have tried it, believe it may some day find its way into our gardens and public markets.

WILD POTATO VINE, OR *MECHA-MECK*, OR MAN-OF-THE-EARTH

Ipomoea pandurata

THIS member of the morning-glory family and very close relative of the Sweet Potato is found in dry soil in fields, along roadsides, and in open waste lands from Connecticut west to southern Ontario, Michigan, and Kansas, and south to Florida and Texas. The stems, three to twelve feet long, trail on the ground or climb up supports when these are convenient. The petioled leaves are nearly as broad as long, with heart-shaped bases, sharp-pointed, margins entire. Generally a few of the leaves are contracted at the middle, becoming fiddle-shaped or lobed. The large handsome blossoms are white with a pink-purple eye or center. They are sometimes three inches in diameter. In shape, the flowers are like those of the sister plant, the cultivated Morning-Glory. Far beneath the surface of the ground, this plant has a great fleshy root that often weighs from ten to twenty pounds. Like those of the Sweet Potato, the roots of the Wild Potato Vine are brittle and slightly milky when fresh; but unlike them, there is only one root to the vine.

The herbaceous vine dies each autumn, but the root remains in the ground year after year, the greater part of it being below the frost line. In the spring, when the warmth of the sun reaches this reservoir of food, a stem is quickly pushed up through the soil, and the plant spreads its leaves and flowers to the light.

I once dug up a root of the Wild Potato. It extended nearly vertically to a depth of three feet or more. The great fleshy root, resembling a large sweet potato, was two and a half feet long and weighed fifteen pounds. Friends of the writer unearthed a plant in southern New Jersey that weighed more than thirty pounds. I also dug out a smaller root and roasted it in my campfire. It much resembled a sweet potato but had a slightly bitter taste. The Indians named this plant the Mecha-meck, and without doubt it was a favorite food among them. They could easily roast the fleshy roots in the ashes of their campfires. They may be used any time during the summer.

The Bush Morning-Glory, Ipomoea leptophylla, which grows on the plains just east of the Rocky Mountains from South Dakota and Montana south to Texas and New Mexico, has an even larger root than the Wild Potato. It is eaten by the western Indians when food is scarce. They roast the roots, which are said to be not very palatable. The roots are difficult to extract from the ground.

Ipomoea Jalapa, another wild morning-glory native of the south Atlantic states, is reported to have a root that weighs from forty to fifty pounds, but I know nothing of its edible qualities.

EDIBLE VALERIAN
Valeriana edulis

The Edible Valerian is an erect, strong-smelling plant, that has a deep carrot-shaped perennial root. It grows from one to four feet tall with few stem leaves. The basal leaves are spatulate, thick, almost fleshy, four to twelve inches long, with the margin fringed with hairs. The stem leaves are parted or cut into three to seven narrow divisions. The small yellowish white flowers are arranged in a long interrupted panicle.

The Edible Valerian is a native from Ontario to Ohio and west to the Pacific Coast. In the mountain regions, it is said to extend as far south as New Mexico and Arizona. It is sometimes cultivated for food in the eastern states and is escaping. It inhabits wet plains and prairies, blooming from May to July.

The root of this plant is six to twelve inches long, bright yellow inside, black outside, shaped like that of a carrot or parsnip. It was one of the chief edible roots of the Indians west of the Rocky Mountains. It is nutritious but is reputed to be agreeable only to some people. The Indians collected the roots in the spring and baked them. The baking process is said to remove the bitterness, making them sweet and wholesome. Dr. Edward Sturtevant says that when cooked, it is "sweet, palatable, and nutritious."

CHICORY
Cichorium Intybus
Described under Salad Plants and Potherbs.

JERUSALEM ARTICHOKE, OR EARTH APPLE
Helianthus tuberosus

The Jerusalem Artichoke is a perennial sunflower, native of America, that grows from six to ten feet high, branching above.

The ovate or oblong leaves have a sharp tapering point, and are rough, hairy above. The yellow flower heads, often numerous, are from two to three inches across. The rays are from twelve to twenty in number. This plant has fleshy thickened rootstocks bearing edible tubers.

The Artichoke is native from Ontario to Georgia, west to Manitoba, Arkansas, and Kansas. It is also found in places east of the Appalachian Mountains where it has escaped to roadsides and waste lands. The Indians cultivated it for food and probably introduced it in the East. William Saunders, formerly of the United States Department of Agriculture, has the following to say concerning the Jerusalem Artichoke:

This plant has numerous creeping roots, which produce tubers like the common potato; these tubers are of a longish, slightly flattened shape, and are considered to be more nutritious than those of the potato. When properly cooked, they are well flavored, and may be eaten by invalids when other vegetables are denied them. They are used in soups, and they make fine pickles when partially boiled, sliced into half-inch thicknesses, and placed in vinegar. In flavor they do not equal the common potato, but from the productiveness of the plant and its suitability to warm and dry climates, it seems probable that it may become of sufficient importance to secure attention, in selecting particularly valuable varieties with improvement of flavor.

We are all familiar with the cultivated Artichoke. The wild tubers should be collected in autumn.

Without doubt it was the Jerusalem Artichoke that Lewis and Clark describe in their Journal under date of April 9, 1805, when in what is now North Dakota:

When we stopped for dinner the squaw [Sacajawea] went out, and after penetrating with a sharp stick the holes of the mice [probably prairie dogs, possibly gophers], near some driftwood, brought to us a quantity of wild artichokes, which the mice collect and hoard in large numbers. The root is white, of an ovate form, from one to three inches long, and generally of the size of a man's finger, and two, four and sometimes six roots are attached to a single stalk. Its flavor as well as the stalk which issues from it resemble those of the Jerusalem artichoke, except that the latter is much larger.

Selection and tillage explain the larger size of the cultivated variety.

The Showy Sunflower, Helianthus laetiflorus, found from Pennsylvania to Minnesota produces tubers that are said to be little inferior to those of the cultivated artichoke.

ADDITIONAL EDIBLE ROOTS

Florida Arrowroot, or Coontie, Zamia Floridana. This Arrowroot and its very near relative, Zamia pumila, are fernlike or palmlike plants found on the eastern side of the Florida peninsula. The large starchy roots are made into flour which is sometimes sold commercially. The arrowroot was a very important food of the Seminole Indians.

Broad-Leaved Cattail. Typha latifolia. This, the common Cattail, is found in wet or marshy lands throughout most of North America, also in Europe and Asia. The central part of the rootstock, which is mainly starch, was dug, dried, and ground into meal by the Indians. It is said that the early poor settlers of Virginia ate the roots and were fond of them. The roots and lower part of the stem are sometimes eaten in salads. The young fruiting spikes are said to be edible roasted. They are sometimes used as food under the name of "Cossack asparagus." The rind of the young stem, from the root to the height of eighteen inches, is peeled off, and the white tender part within makes a pleasant article of food.

Narrow-Leaved Cattail, Typha angustifolia, is abundant in marsh lands along the Atlantic coast and sometimes inland, also in Europe and Asia. The spikes are taller but more slender than the broad-leaved species. The edible qualities of the plant are the same as those of the last species.

Great American Bulrush, Scirpus validus. Found in swamps and borders of streams and ponds, nearly throughout North America, except the extreme north. The roots are eaten by the Indians of California, Arizona, and the upper Missouri valley.

Green Arrow Arum, or Virginia Tuckahoe, Peltandra virginica. The Arrow Arum grows in swamps and shallow water from Maine to Ontario, south to Florida and Louisiana. The root, which is bulbous, is said to weigh three or four pounds. It is starchy with the biting qualities of the Indian Turnip. According to Captain John Smith, it was much used by the Indians of Virginia, who roasted it in pits for a day or two. After cooking, the roots were generally dried and ground into meal. It is also said that the Indians ate the boiled spadix and berries as a luxury.

Water Arum, or Wild Calla, Calla palustris. Native in bogs from Nova Scotia to Minnesota, south to New Jersey, Ohio, and Iowa, also in Europe and Asia. The root has the acrid qualities of the last species. Missen bread is made in Lapland from roots of this plant.

Golden Club, or Taw-kee (Indian), Orontium aquaticum. Found in swamps and ponds from Massachusetts to Pennsylvania and south to Florida and Louisiana, generally along the coast. The bulbous rootstocks are edible when cooked. The dried seeds, which resemble peas, were eaten by both Indian and white colonists. This was after repeated boilings.

Amole, or Wild Potato, or Soap Plant, Chlorogalum pomeridianum. This member of the lily family has an egg-shaped bulb from one to three inches in diameter. It is called Soap Plant because "its fibrous-coated bulb, which forms a lather with water, may be used in washing" (Harvey M. Hall). Cooking is said to destroy the acrid properties of the bulb, making it a good wholesome food. It is native of California.

Wild Hyacinth, or Blue Dicks, or Cluster Lily, or Grassnut, Brodiaea capitata. This close relative of the onion is common throughout California. The bulbs are said to be very good when cooked slowly for half an hour. Dr. Harvey M. Hall says: "The small bulbs, known as grass-nuts, are often eaten by children who, like the Indians, prefer them uncooked."

Harvest Brodiaea, Brodiaea grandiflora, *Hookera coronaria,* is common in fields and meadows from Washington south to central California. Charles F. Saunders says of it: "Its bulbs are best cooked, as by slow roasting in hot ashes, which develops the sweetness."

Turk's-Cap Lily, Lilium superbum. This beautiful wild lily is found from New Brunswick to Minnesota, south to North Carolina and Missouri, generally growing along streams. The fleshy bulbs were eaten by the Indians, who often used them in thickening soups, according to Thoreau.

Wild Yellow Lily, or Canada Lily, Lilium canadense. This beautiful wild flower is found in meadows and low grounds from Nova Scotia to Minnesota, south to Georgia and Missouri. Bulbs are edible when cooked. This and the last species should be protected; therefore they should be used only as emergency foods.

Yellow Adder's-Tongue, or Fawn Lily, Erythronium americanum. Found in moist woods and along streams from Nova Scotia to Minnesota, south to Florida and Arkansas. The bulb is edible when cooked, and the leaves are sometimes used for greens. This should be used only as an emergency food.

Star-of-Bethlehem, Ornithogalum umbellatum. Introduced from Europe and Asia, now often abundant in fields and meadows from New Hampshire to Pennsylvania and Virginia. The bulbs are pleasant and nutritious when cooked. They are often eaten in eastern Europe and western Asia.

China Brier, or Long-Stalked Greenbrier, Smilax pseudo-china. Found in dry or sandy soil from Southern New Jersey to Kansas, south to Florida and Texas. The starchy tuberous roots were ground fine by the Indians, then water was added and the whole strained through a basket. When the water was evaporated, a fine reddish meal remained. According to Bartram, "A small quantity of this, mixed with warm water and sweetened with honey, when cool, becomes a beautiful delicious jelly, very nourishing and wholesome. They also mix it with fine corn flour, which being fried in fresh bear's grease, makes very good hot cakes or fritters."

Bristly Greenbrier, Smilax Bona-nox. This Greenbrier grows in thickets from New Jersey to Missouri, south to Florida and Texas. The large tuberous roots were ground into meal by the Indians and used for bread or gruel.

Utah Aloe. Agave utahensis. Found in Utah, Arizona, Nevada to eastern California. The large bulbous root is considered a delicacy by the Indians. When properly prepared and roasted, it is said to be sweet and delicious.

Seacoast Abronia, Abronia latifolia, *Abronia arenaria*. This is a seashore plant from Vancouver to California. The long stout roots are eaten by the Chinook Indians.

Spring Beauty, Claytonia virginica. This beautiful wild flower of spring is found in open woods from Nova Scotia to Saskatchewan, south to Florida and Texas. The small starchy bulbs were much prized by the Indians. Although the plants are often abundant, yet they should be preserved.

Broad-Leaved Spring Beauty, Claytonia caroliniana. Found over much the same range as the last species but not extending so far south nor so abundant. The roots are edible.

Rue Anemone, Anemonella thalictroides, *Syndesmon thalictroides*. This delicate spring flower is found from New Hampshire to Minnesota, south to Florida, Tennessee, and Kansas. The starchy tuberous roots are edible when cooked. I know of mountainous districts in Pennsylvania where these roots are collected and eaten under the name of "wild potato." The plant should be protected.

American Sea Rocket, Cakile edentula. Found along the seashore from Newfoundland to Florida and along the Great Lakes from New York to Minnesota; also on the coast of California. In times past, in Canada, when food was scarce, the fleshy root is said to have been ground, mixed with flour and made into bread. The fleshy leaves of this plant, like those of many other plants in the mustard family, are sometimes used as a potherb, or in salads.

Silverweed, or Goose Tansy, Potentilla Anserina, *Argentina Anserina*. Found on river banks and lake shores, also in brackish marshes from Greenland to New Jersey, west to Alaska and New Mexico, also in California and in Europe and Asia. The roots are edible and wholesome. J. Lightfoot remarked: "Boiled or roasted, they taste like parsnips. In Hebrides, the roots have often supported the inhabitants for months together."

Wild Licorice, or American Licorice, Glycyrrhiza lepidota. The American Wild Licorice is native from Hudson Bay to British Columbia, south to Missouri, northern Mexico, and California. The long fleshy perennial roots are sweet and are eaten by the Indians. They closely resemble the roots of the cultivated licorice, *Glycyrrhiza glabra,* of Europe and Asia. I have chewed the fleshy roots of this plant in the southwestern United States and found them pleasing. In New Mexico, I found it growing near the Indian villages as though once cultivated.

Licorice Root, Hedysarum Mackenzii, is found in central Canada west to Alaska. Its long flexible roots are sweet, resembling licorice and are much eaten in spring by the Indians. This is the wild licorice of the trappers of the Northwest. Hedysarum boreale, a closely related species, is found in southern Canada and the extreme northern United States. It can probably be used in the same way as the northwestern species.

Pimple Mallow, Callirhoe pedata, of the northwestern states. The roots resemble those of a parsnip and are used for food by the Indians from Nebraska to Idaho.

Evening Primrose, Oenothera biennis. The Evening Primrose is native from Labrador to Minnesota, south to Florida and Texas. It was introduced from America into Europe as early as 1614 and was formerly cultivated in English gardens for its edible roots which, when boiled, are said to be wholesome and nutritious. In Germany, after its introduction, the roots were used for food and the young shoots for salads. It was recommended to American gardeners under name of German Rampion.

Smooth Sweet Cicely, or Sweet Myrrh, Osmorhiza longistylis, *Washingtonia longistylis*. This plant ranges from Nova Scotia to Assiniboia, south to Alabama and Kansas. The root has the spicy taste of anise and is often chewed by boys. The roots should be gathered with caution, for sometimes the deadly poison Hemlock or the Water Hemlock is mistaken for it. It does not grow in wet ground.

Water Parsley, Oenanthe sarmentosa. The Water Parsley is found from British Columbia to central California. "The tubers form one of the dainty dishes of the Oregon Indians." Boiled like potatoes, they are sweet, starchy, with a slight flavor of parsley. Be certain that you have the right species.

Gamote or Camote, Cymopterus montanus, found in the southwestern United States and northern Mexico. "Root parsnip-like, softer, sweeter, and more tender than the parsnip." The root is much used by Mexicans and Indians.

Wild Potato, Solanum fendleri, *Solanum tuberosum boreale*. Common in the mountainous sections of New Mexico and Arizona. The tubers, which are about the size of marbles or grapes, are edible when boiled or roasted and are said to resemble in taste boiled chestnuts. They are much used by the Navajo Indians. It is suggested that this species may be the original of the cultivated Potato. Solanum Jamesii, a similar plant growing over much the same range, but extending farther north, also has small edible tubers.

Broomrape, Orobanche ludoviciana. This parasite grows on the roots of plants in sandy soil from Illinois to South Dakota, south and west to Texas and California. All the plant except the fruiting part grows underground; therefore the thick stems are white and tender. They are much consumed by the Pah Ute Indians.

Salsify, or Purple Oyster Plant. Tragopogon porrifolius. A native of Europe, escaped from cultivation in the northern United States and on the Pacific Coast. The roots when tender may be used for food. The tops are sometimes used for greens. The Yellow Salsify, Tragopogon pratensis, also escaped, has been used like the purple species.

Balsam Root, or Oregon Sunflower, Balsamorhiza sagittata. Montana to Washington, south to Colorado and California. The Nez Percé Indians cook the fleshy roots on hot stones. They are said to be sweet and quite agreeable in taste.

Hooker's Balsam Root, Balsamorhiza hookeri, which grows from Washington to Utah and California, is a similar plant. The Indians often eat the roots raw, but they are more pleasant when cooked.

Indian Thistle, Cirsium edule, *Carduus edulis*. The roots of this thistle were formerly eaten by the Indians from California to Washington. The Elk Thistle, Cirsium foliosum, which grows from

Washington to Wyoming and north, also has an edible root. In 1870, when Truman Everts was lost for more than a month in the region of Yellowstone Park, the roots of this plant more than anything else kept him from starving.

BEVERAGE AND FLAVORING PLANTS

NOTHING is more refreshing to the tired camper than a cup of hot tea, especially if the day has been spent in tramping. Should one have forgotten or exhausted his supply, then Nature's offerings are welcome, and many wild plants may be used for this purpose. I was once camping with some prospectors in the southern Sierra Nevada Mountains when our supply of Oriental tea ran short. The nearest place that it could be obtained was nearly seventy-five miles away. For a week we had a different kind of tea almost every night, using wild plants that were familiar to the miners, and that they knew were used for beverages. At least two varieties were quite acceptable.

One quickly gets tired of almost any kind of food after eating it for several meals in succession, and a change is a great relief; but it is not so with beverages such as tea and coffee. I have known people that have had their coffee every morning for years without missing once. I believe it is possible for a person to become accustomed to drinking tea from wild plants; and the longer they were used the better they would be relished. Our forefathers often went through hard privations for food and beverages. (I know that mine did, for they all went west of the Appalachian Mountains when it was nothing but an Indian wilderness.) When commercial tea could not be obtained, they relied upon the bountiful supply of Nature. During the Civil War many people, both North and South, made tea from native plants, and wheat, corn, and rye were roasted and ground for "coffee." During the Revolutionary War the Americans did not take kindly to Oriental tea flavored with an English tax, and beverages from many wild plants came into use. Even the American Indians relish drinks made from native plants.

Spices from far-off India, used for seasoning, were also scarce in the interior of our country. Mints and other fragrant plants were brought from abroad and planted about the homes; but when the old-fashioned herb garden failed to supply the proper materials, then the native wild mints and other aromatic plants were pressed into service.

BLACK, SWEET, OR CHERRY BIRCH

Betula lenta

I bring sweet thoughts of birchen trees
Growing by stream and fountain.

THE Black Birch is a large forest tree sometimes eighty feet high with a diameter of two feet, with dark bark, smooth in young trees but becoming cracked or furrowed in old ones. The bark of younger trees much resembles that of the cultivated Sweet Cherry. Both the bark and foliage have the sweet aroma of Wintergreen. The leaves are ovate or ovate-oblong, long-pointed at the apex, base somewhat heart-shaped, silky when young, short-petioled, edges doubly serrate. The staminate catkins are two to four inches long, pendent. Fruiting catkins erect, sessile, cylindric, about an inch long, and half an inch thick. Found from Maine to western Ontario, south to Delaware, Indiana, and Iowa, and in the mountains to Alabama and Tennessee.

While the Black Birch grows best in rich, rather moist woods, it can adapt itself to a variety of conditions, often starting on old logs or stumps or perched on rocks or growing from cracks or seams of rocks.

Dr. Alphonso Wood, the American botanist, wrote of the Black Birch: "In spring the cambium affords the boys a delicious morsel." It is not only in the spring, for the inner bark has the sweet, spicy, wintergreen flavor at all times; but at that season of the year the bark easily separates from the wood and is generally eaten by the boys. The Black Birch makes a most delightful tea, the same in taste as that of Mountain Tea or Wintergreen. For this purpose, the rapidly growing young twigs are generally used. The thick inner bark from the trunk is good, but to remove it injures and disfigures the tree. When boys, we often gathered birch for tea (when we could induce Mother to make it for us) and generally preferred the bark from the larger roots. This bark is almost red, easily separates from the wood in spring and early summer, and is strongly flavored. It may be dried and kept for months without losing much of its spicy taste. Sugar and cream added to the tea is preferred by most people. Large quantities of the oil of wintergreen are distilled from the twigs and bark of the Black Birch. The essence is exactly the same as that produced from the true Wintergreen (*Gaultheria*).

The sap of the Black Birch may be used for making sugar. It is only about half as sweet as that obtained from the Sugar Maple. It flows freely in April, or about a month later than that of maple trees.

It is claimed that in 1861, after the Battle of Carricks Ford, the edible bark of Black Birch probably saved the lives of hundreds of Garnett's Confederate soldiers during their retreat over the mountains to Monterey, Virginia. For a number of years after that, the route the soldiers took could be traced by the peeled birch trees.

The Yellow Birch, Betula lutea, is a larger tree than the Black Birch and is much more abundant in our northern states. The bark has a yellowish tinge, in younger trees often separating in thin layers. The fruiting catkins are larger than those of the Black Birch. This tree is found from Newfoundland to Manitoba, south to New Jersey and Illinois, and in the mountains to Tennessee. The bark has the spicy wintergreen flavor but not so pronounced as in the Black Birch.

In Maine the Indians make a tea from the leaves of the Paper or Canoe Birch, Betula papyrifera, as recorded by Henry D. Thoreau in *The Maine Woods,* and seem to greatly relish it.

SASSAFRAS, OR AGUE TREE

Sassafras variifolium

Sassafras Sassafras

PROBABLY few species of trees are better known to country people than the Sassafras. It is found in dry soil, preferring a sandy loam, from Massachusetts to Michigan, Iowa, and Kansas, south to Florida and Texas. I recently found quite large trees twenty-five miles north of Galveston. It is generally a small tree in the northern part of its range but often grows large in the South. In northern New Jersey, I have seen trees nearly three feet in diameter. The larger trees have thick, rough, reddish brown bark, broken in broad flat ridges. The twigs and young shoots are bright green, mucilaginous.

The alternate leaves are of three forms: oval and entire, mitten-shaped—that is, with one lobe on the side—or three-lobed, the larger lobe in the middle. All three forms are on the same tree, often on the same twig. The petioles are generally less than an inch long. The flowers are in umbeled racemes, unfolding with the leaves or just before the leaves appear. The flowers are dioecious—stamens and pistils on separate trees. Apparently the staminate trees are much the more numerous. The blossoms are greenish yellow, about a quarter of an inch across with a spicy odor. The ripe drupe or berry, on a thick red stem, is dark blue, nearly half an inch high. The leaves, twigs, bark, and berries all have a rich, spicy odor, or as Clinton Scollard, the poet says:

> When the sassafras you bruise
> There's perfume fit to fill a cruse.

This tree is generally found along roadsides, in fence corners, and along borders of woods. The roots are rather deep, throwing up numerous suckers often forming thickets.

The bark of the Sassafras root is distilled in large quantities for the oil, which is used in flavoring medicines, scenting perfumery,

Sassafras (Sassafras variifolium)

making candy, etc. It also has a medicinal use and is often sold in drugstores. In the South, the leaves are dried and used for thickening and flavoring soups, especially in creole cookery, the veins or hard parts being discarded. The bark of the root makes an excellent tea, especially when served with sugar and cream. Country people often drink it in the springtime with the belief that it purifies the blood. During the Civil War it was much used, especially in the South, when tea from the Orient could not be obtained.

It is stated that the Sassafras was first discovered by Bartholomew Gosnold, the English explorer, in 1602, on Cuttyhunk Island, one of the Elizabeth Islands off the coast of southern Massachusetts. Gosnold is said to have transported several trees back to England, where they were sold for three shillings a pound. Sassafras root is believed to have been the first plant product exported from New England.

During colonial days Sassafras root was in great demand in Europe, and it became an important article of commerce. It was used for tea and flavoring and was long sold in the stores of London. The name Sassafras is of Spanish origin, and the tree probably received it during the early Spanish explorations.

We have bought Sassafras root in the country markets of Pennsylvania and have seen it for sale elsewhere. In 1937, at least one carload of these roots was shipped to the Pacific Coast.

Julia E. Rogers in *The Tree Book* says: "Who has not nibbled the dainty green buds of sassafras in winter, or dug at the roots for a bit of their aromatic bark? Or who has not searched among the leaves for mittens? Surely they are people whose youth was spent in regions that knew not this little tree of the fence corners and woodland borders. And they have missed something very much worth while out of their childhood."

SPICEBUSH, OR WILD ALLSPICE

Benzoin aestivale

Benzoin Benzoin

THE Spicebush is a common shrub that grows from five to fifteen feet high, with smooth, dark bark, and slender, brittle twigs. Usually several stems develop from the same clump of roots, forming a round-topped globular cluster. It prefers rich, moist soil, often growing where it is quite swampy. It is native from Maine to Michigan, south to Georgia, Tennessee, and Kansas. Like most familiar shrubs and plants, it goes under a variety of names in different localities. Others than those mentioned above are Benjamin Bush, Spicewood, Feverbush, Snapwood, or merery Spice.

The oval or oblong alternate leaves are dark green, smooth, with entire edges. The apex is pointed, the base tapering, the petioles short. The veins are depressed above, prominent below. The flowers, in dense clusters, appear before the leaves, or in March or April. They are yellow, spicily scented. The blossoms have no petals, but the calyx is six-parted. Like its near relative, the Sassafras (both are members of the laurel family), stamens and pistils are on separate shrubs. The stamens are nine to a blossom, arranged in three sets or rows. The pistil forms a bright scarlet, oval drupe or

Spicebush (Benzoin aestivale)

berry, less than half an inch long, containing one large seed of the same shape. The entire berry is oily and aromatic.

The Spicebush is decorative and should do well in cultivation. The numerous yellow blossoms and red berries are pleasing, and the dark green leaves of summer turn golden yellow in autumn.

The leaves, twigs, bark, and berries of Spicebush have a strong aromatic odor and taste. In earlier days it was used in medicines, but it is doubtful if the plant has any particular virtue in that respect. It is used for tea, however, especially in the South. During the Civil War, it was much used as a substitute for tea both by the soldiers and by their friends at home. They used the leaves as well as twigs and bark. The pioneers also used it in colonizing the American wilderness. André Michaux, the French botanist, in traveling through the American wilderness wrote in his journal February 9, 1796, after stopping at a settler's cabin: "I had supped the previous evening on tea made from the shrub called Spicewood. A handful of young twigs or branches is set to boil and after it has boiled at least a quarter of an hour, sugar is added and it is drunk like tea. I was told that milk makes it much more agreeable to the taste. This beverage restores strength, and it had that effect, for I was very tired when I arrived."

I have made tea from both twigs and bark of the Spicebush and find that when sugar and cream are added, it makes quite a pleasant drink. However, I prefer Sassafras or Wintergreen. It is claimed that at the time of the American Revolution the berries were dried, powdered, and used as a substitute for allspice.

SWEET BAY, OR RED BAY, OR LAUREL, OR ISABELLA WOOD

Persea Borbonia

A THIRD member of the laurel family (the one to which the Sassafras and Spicebush belong) is the Sweet Bay, which is found from Delaware to Florida, west to Texas and as far north as Arkansas. It grows along streams and in swamps near the coast, apparently never away from the coastal plain. It is sometimes shrublike, but usually is a small tree, thirty to fifty or even sixty feet high, with dark reddish brown bark in flat ridges. The evergreen leaves are two to five inches long, about one-third as wide, often rather long-pointed at both ends. They are somewhat leathery with entire margins, bright green above, pale beneath. The petioles are a third of an inch to an inch long. From the axils of the leaves arise small panicles of yellowish green perfect flowers. By "perfect" we mean pistil and stamens are in the same flower. The Sassafras and Spicebush are both dioecious; that is, pistils on one tree or bush, stamens on another. The blue, one-seeded berries on red pedicels are quite like those of the Sassafras but are a little larger, about half an inch in diameter. All parts of the tree are aromatic.

The dried leaves of the bay tree are much used in cooking, especially in the South. They are exceptionally important in Creole cookery. In almost any grocery or drugstore in the country, at least in those that sell spices, one can buy packages of Sweet Bay or Laurel leaves. They are supposed to be from the Sweet Bay or Laurel of southern Europe, Laurus nobilis, famed in song and story, whose leaves were used to crown Greek heroes. The European Laurel and the southern Sweet Bay are closely related, and I find practically no difference in the flavor produced by each. Friends of the writer in southeastern Texas who used both the leaves of the wild Sweet Bay of the South and the store material are under the impression that they not only are alike but come from the American tree.

The name Laurel is rather unfortunate in this connection, for the Mountain Laurel (Kalmia latifolia), a shrub belonging to an entirely different family of plants, is somewhat poisonous, while the Sweet Bay not only is harmless but gives off a pleasing aroma wherever employed. The leaves are used in confections and to flavor roasts and stews, also in "stuffing" or dressing for roast fowl and other meats. They are used to flavor certain types of soups, especially crab gumbo.

Many people prefer to collect and dry their own leaves. The best time for this purpose is early summer just after the new growth has been made, although they can be gathered at any season since the tree is evergreen. The leaves should be carefully gathered and washed, then spread out to dry. When thoroughly dry they may be kept for a year or two. We collected some in Texas and used them when the occasion demanded.

The Sweet Bay has been in favor since colonial times. The southern colonists probably learned its use because it so closely resembles the Laurel or Sweet Bay of Europe, or they may have learned its use from the Indians. In passing, it may be of interest to know that the Avocado, or Alligator Pear (Persea gratissima), is a brother of the Sweet Bay described above; both are members of the same genus.

APPLE (FOR CIDER)

Pyrus malus

Described under Edible Wild Fruits.

KENTUCKY COFFEE TREE, OR CHICOT, OR AMERICAN COFFEE BEAN

Gymnocladus dioica

The Kentucky Coffee Tree reaches a maximum diameter of nearly three feet and a height of about ninety feet. The great majority of trees are much smaller. The gray bark is rough, rather deeply fissured, often covered with rather thin recurved scales. The leaves are doubly compound and sometimes are nearly three feet long and two feet wide. The secondary leafstalks have each from seven to fifteen leaflets. The ovate leaflets are rounded at the base, sharp-pointed, with entire or wavy margins. The greenish white flowers in terminal racemes appear in June. The legumes or seed pods are reddish brown with a grayish bloom, five to eight inches long, an inch and a half wide, flattened but quite heavy. There are six to nine seeds, each surrounded by a dark sweetish pulp. The slightly oval flattish seeds are nearly three-fourths of an inch long, grayish brown, very hard.

The Kentucky Coffee Tree ranges from central New York to South Dakota, south to Tennessee and Oklahoma. It is planted as a shade or ornamental tree farther east. As a wild tree it is rather rare, and one is much more likely to find it in cultivation. It prefers a rich, moist soil, and usually grows in lowlands along streams. This is one of the last trees to come out in leaf in the spring and drops its leaves quite early in autumn. The branchlets are few and stout corresponding to the size of the leaf. The French Canadians call it Chicot, which means "stump," and the generic name means "naked branch"; the tree is without leaves such a long period of the year. The large seed pods on thick stems generally remain on the tree all winter.

The pioneers apparently made much use of the seeds of this tree, which were roasted and ground, then used as a substitute for coffee. This was in the interior of our country before and during the Revolutionary War. Kentucky was settled early, when it was practically impossible to get commercial coffee to that region. It is claimed that the seeds were roasted and eaten by the Indians. It is also recorded that Long's expedition to the Rocky Mountains in 1820, when encamped on the Missouri River, used these seeds as a substitute for coffee and found the drink wholesome and palatable.

STAGHORN SUMAC, OR LEMONADE TREE
Rhus hirta
Rhus typhina

THE sumacs are well known to most country people. The common Staghorn Sumac is our largest species, growing to a height of more than thirty feet and a diameter of nearly six inches. The young twigs are densely covered with velvety hairs resembling the horns of a stag in appearance and mode of branching. The bark is smooth, the juice or sap milky, the pith large, and the wood orange streaked with green. The pinnate leaves are about twenty inches long with eleven to twenty-nine leaflets, the average number being about twenty-one. The oblong-lanceolate leaflets are three to five inches long, sharp-pointed, rounded at the base with saw-toothed edges. They are dark green above and pale beneath. The flowers

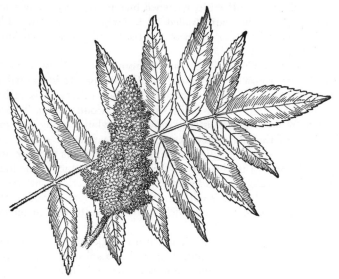

Staghorn Sumac (Rhus typhina)

occur in dense terminal panicles. The blossoms are small, yellowish green. The calyx is five-lobed, and the corolla has five petals. The blooming period is June—sometimes later. Some trees bear stamens only, and others have the pistillate blossoms. The staminate panicles are sometimes nearly a foot long and spreading. The fertile panicles are smaller and very dense, making a compact fruit cluster. The small, one-seeded drupes, or berries, covered with crimson hairs, mature early in autumn and remain on the trees all winter.

The Staghorn Sumac grows in dry, gravelly, or rocky soil from Nova Scotia to South Dakota, and south to Georgia, Indiana, and Iowa. It is generally clustered, spreading by the roots, in thickets, along the borders of woods, fences, or frequently in old fields. It grows rapidly but is short-lived.

The fruit of the Staghorn Sumac is very sour; hence the name

Vinegar Tree which is sometimes applied to this species. When the berries are placed in water for a short time, a pleasing and agreeable drink is formed, known to boys as "Indian lemonade." For this purpose the berries are best in late summer or early autumn.

The Smooth or Scarlet Sumac, Rhus glabra, is a shrub five to fifteen feet tall. It is quite similar to the Staghorn in general appearance, especially at a distance, but the young twigs are smooth with a pale bluish or whitish bloom. The flower and fruiting panicles are also quite similar to those of the Staghorn. The fruits have the same sour taste and are just as good for making Indian lemonade. They are sometimes used as a substitute for lemon juice. The Smooth Sumac is common in neglected fields, along roadsides and borders of woods, from Nova Scotia to Minnesota, south to Florida and Louisiana.

The Dwarf or Mountain Sumac, Rhus copallina, is a shrub or, in the southern part of its range, sometimes a small tree. It is quite similar to the two preceding species, but the rachis, or leaf stem, to which the leaflets are attached is wing-margined—a feature that distinguishes it from the other sumacs. It grows in dry soil from Maine to Minnesota, south to Florida and Texas. It is generally most common in mountainous regions. Its panicles of bright red fruits may also be used for making Indian lemonade.

THE FRAGRANT OR SWEET-SCENTED SUMAC

Rhus canadensis

Rhus aromatica

Schmaltzia crenata

THE Fragrant Sumac is a sweet-scented shrub usually only a few feet high. The leaves have three leaflets which are aromatic when crushed. The bright red fruits, which occur in small clusters, are very acid. I know by experiment that they can be used in making Indian lemonade. The Fragrant Sumac is a shrub of rocky situations from Vermont, Ontario, and Minnesota, south to Florida and Texas.

The Ill-Scented Sumac, or Squawbush, Rhus trilobata, *Schmaltzia trilobata,* is very similar to the last species and by many botanists is considered only a variety of it. It is native from Illinois to Texas, west to the Pacific Coast. Dr. Harvey M. Hall in his *Yosemite Flora* says of this shrub: "The Squaw Bush is of great service to the

Indians who utilize the split stems in basketry and who prepare a refreshing beverage by soaking the berries in water."

The Poison Ivy, Rhus toxicodendron, the Poison Oak, Rhus quercifolia, and the Poison Sumac, Rhus vernix, all have white fruits and cannot well be confused with any of the above described species, all of which have red fruits.

LEMONADE BERRY

Rhus integrifolia

THICKETS of this shrub are often found on hillsides and growing about the sand dunes of southern California. It does not extend far back from the coast. The evergreen leaves are rounded at the apex. The red berries are arranged in stiff panicled spikes. They are larger than those of most other sumacs and excrete an acid substance that, when soaked in water, makes an excellent drink. The Indians made use of it, as do boys of this age. I have tried the beverage and find it a good substitute for lemonade.

NEW JERSEY TEA, OR REDROOT

Ceanothus americanus

THE New Jersey Tea is a common shrub that inhabits dry sandy or gravelly soil in open woods and thickets from Maine to Manitoba, south to Florida and Texas. The upright stems, usually several from the same root cluster, are one to three feet tall. The alternate ovate leaves are two or three inches long, less than half as wide, pointed at the apex, base often heart-shaped, edges sawtoothed, rather strongly three-nerved. The small white flowers appear about the first of June. They are arranged in small dense panicles on the ends of the branches. The shrub is conspicuous in blossom. In fact, it is attractive and decorative in cultivation. Few wild flowers attract such a variety of insects as the blossoms of the New Jersey Tea. The red root makes an excellent dye.

This plant was used as a substitute for tea during the American Revolution, especially by the soldiers, when Oriental tea, brought in English vessels, was very unpopular, and its use considered unpatriotic. The leaves were dried, and an infusion made from them which was very palatable, but certainly not so pleasant as that of real tea. However, it is a good substitute, and no doubt would

cheer and refresh a tired soldier camping under unfavorable conditions.

I have made tea from both the green and the dried leaves; the
latter are the better, and cream and sugar improve the flavor. When
I was discussing colonial life and customs before a women's club,
the refreshment committee, at the close of the meeting, served New
Jersey tea made from leaves which I had previously gathered and
dried. It added much interest to the meeting; and of the hundred
or more women who partook of this colonial beverage, some seemed
to enjoy it and spoke highly of its flavor.

CASSENA, OR YAUPON, OR INDIAN BLACK DRINK

Ilex vomitoria

THE Yaupon is an evergreen holly of the southern states found
in swamps and along streams near the coast from Virginia to Florida,
west to Arkansas and Texas. It is generally a shrub, sometimes a
small tree, and often is so abundant as to form dense thickets. The
leathery leaves are small, usually little more than an inch long,
elliptic in outline with crenate or wavy edges. They are deep green
and shining above, pale beneath. The petioles are about an eighth
of an inch long. The small white flowers are in short axillary clusters. There are four sepals, four corolla lobes, and four stamens.
The red berries are about one-fourth inch in diameter, or a little
smaller than those of the Holly (*Ilex opaca*).

From the leaves of this shrub, the American Indians obtained
their famous black drink. For this purpose the leaves were dried
and often toasted. It apparently was an article of trade among the
Indians, and in the interior of the country was used by the native
tribes on both sides of the Mississippi River. The leaves are often
used for tea along the south Atlantic coast and sometimes can be
purchased in the markets. When very strong, the tea occasionally
acts as an emetic. The shrub is a very close relative of the Maté,
or Paraguay Tea (Ilex paraguayensis), and the beverage is said to
be quite like that of the latter plant. As the shrub is evergreen, the
leaves may be gathered at any season.

In southeastern Texas, where this shrub is abundant and goes
under the name of Yaupon, I collected the leaves, washed and dried
them. I cared little for the tea made from them; neither did I like
the Paraguay tea which I secured for comparison. To me, the flavor

of the two was quite alike. Both are said to be stimulating beverages, and I think a person could develop a liking for them.

DAHOON HOLLY
Ilex Cassine

THE Dahoon Holly is a shrub found in swamps along the Atlantic and Gulf coasts from Virginia to Louisiana. In some respects it is quite like the species described above; but the evergreen leaves are larger, oblong, entire or sometimes toothed toward the apex. The leaves are used for tea and are said to be sold in the markets along the south Atlantic coast. The Creek Indians were apparently fond of the tea made from the toasted leaves.

LABRADOR TEA
Ledum groenlandicum

THE Labrador Tea is a beautiful evergreen shrub that grows from one to three feet high. The twigs are densely covered with wool. The alternate entire leaves are oblong in outline, blunt or rounded at the end with the margins rolled in. They are one to two inches long, dark green above, densely covered with light brown wool beneath. The foliage is quite thick and leathery, and fragrant when crushed in the hand.

The flowers of the Labrador Tea, which appear in early summer, are on the ends of the twigs in short umbel-like clusters. The numerous blossoms, less than half an inch across, are white, with five spreading petals. The small calyx is five-toothed; there are usually five stamens and a five-celled seed pod.

This shrub is found growing in swamps, bogs, and damp woods from Greenland and Labrador southwest to Connecticut, Pennsylvania, Michigan, Minnesota, and Washington. It is common northward, but in the southern part of its range is confined chiefly to mountain swamps and bogs. It is said to have been used as a tea during the Revolutionary War. I recently collected some in a mountain bog in northern Pennsylvania and tested it out after the leaves were dried. The tea had a slight aroma and a taste (to me) somewhat like Oriental tea. It was not disagreeable, and I think could be enjoyed by the camper. When a little lemon was added, it made a fairly good iced tea. In speaking of this shrub, one author says its juices are "bitter, astringent, and narcotic." The tea pre-

Labrador Tea (Ledum groenlandicum)

pared by me showed none of these qualities; however, there was apparently a slight physiological effect, and I would not advise drinking more than a cup of this tea at one time. The Western Labrador Tea, Ledum glandulosum, is said to be poisonous.

WINTERGREEN, OR MOUNTAIN TEA
Gaultheria procumbens

DESCRIBED under Edible Wild Fruits.

CREEPING SNOWBERRY
Chiogenes hispidula

DESCRIBED under Edible Wild Fruits.

SPEARMINT, OR COMMON MINT
Mentha spicata

THE Spearmint, well known to the ancients, is a native of Europe and Asia, but was introduced into this country more than two hundred years ago and is now well established. It may be found along watercourses and in wet places from Nova Scotia to Washington on the Pacific Coast, south to Florida, Texas, and California.

This is a smooth perennial with creeping roots. It grows from one to two feet tall, branched, with opposite lanceolate leaves. The leaves are sessile or nearly so, toothed, long-pointed or sharp at the apex, narrowed at the base. The pale purple flowers are whorled in slender, terminal, interrupted spikes.

The Spearmint, like the other species of this genus, is used more for flavoring than it is for a beverage. The oil is distilled in the same manner as that of Peppermint and is used for flavoring chewing gum and candies. This plant is often grown in gardens for household use and is served with vinegar as a sauce for roast lamb. In some parts of the country, it is called Lamb Mint. Sprigs of it are often used for making mint julep and mint jelly.

The American Wild Mint, Mentha canadensis, found from New Brunswick to Virginia, west to the Pacific Coast, is a common plant in low or marshy ground. It is sometimes cultivated in gardens for its fragrant odor and pleasing taste. It is used for flavoring. The Indians of Maine roasted the leaves before a fire and ate them with salt in the belief that they were nourishing.

PEPPERMINT
Mentha piperita

WE are all familiar with the taste and odor of peppermint, but not many people know the plant as it grows along brooksides and ditches and in wet places. It is a perennial spreading by creeping rootstocks. The square stems characteristic of the mint family grow from one to two feet tall. They are usually purplish, branching near the summit. The opposite leaves, on short petioles, are ovate-lanceolate, with sharp-toothed edges and pointed apex. They are from one to three inches long and about half as wide, very strongly scented with peppermint. The flowers are in terminal spikes, one to three inches long, generally dense but sometimes loose or interrupted. The numerous purple-pink blossoms are nearly a quarter of an inch long or about the same length as the four stamens.

The Peppermint is native of Europe and Asia but was early introduced into America and is now a common plant from Nova Scotia to Florida, west to Minnesota and Arkansas. It is largely cultivated for the pungent oil found in glands in the leaves. This is obtained by pressure and distillation. Southern Michigan is the center of the peppermint oil industry, and is said to produce half of the world's supply of peppermint oil. Northern Indiana and the southern part of New York State also produce it. Peppermint is much more used in candy making than any other flavoring substance. It also has a medicinal value. The leaves are sometimes used for seasoning and the plant is occasionally grown in gardens for this purpose. The householder can get the flavoring from fresh leaves by boiling them in water for a few minutes and using the solution which contains the oil.

CHIA

Salvia columbariae

DESCRIBED under Edible Seeds and Seed Pods.

CHICORY

Cichorium Intybus

DESCRIBED under Salad Plants.

SWEET GOLDENROD

Solidago odora

AMONG all our goldenrods—more than fifty species are found in the northeastern United States—there is at least one that appeals to both sight and smell. It is the Sweet or Anise-Scented Goldenrod, the name being derived not from the flower cluster but from the odor of the crushed leaves. The majority of these plants are striking in appearance but have odors that are not pleasant.

The Sweet Goldenrod ranges from Maine and Vermont south to Florida and west to Missouri and Texas. It grows in fertile but dry or sandy soil along the borders of thickets, in open woods, or on sunny hillsides. It is a slender species, growing only two or three feet high, often reclining. The lanceolate leaves are two to four inches long and about half an inch wide, sessile, sharp-pointed, with entire margins and a prominent midvein. The leaves have numerous tiny clear dots which secrete an aniselike fragrance. The spreading racemes of yellow flowers form a one-sided panicle. It blooms from July to September.

The fragrant leaves, when dried and steeped in water, form a beverage that is quite pleasing. The plant is sometimes referred to as Blue Mountain Tea. I find it recorded that the dried flowers make a pleasant and wholesome tea substitute. Charles F. Saunders in his *Useful Wild Plants* says of this species: "In some parts of the country, the gathering of the leaves to dry and peddle in the winter has formed a minor rural industry, yielding a modest revenue." In Alphonso Wood's *Manual of Botany* we find it recorded: "The only species of solidago which has properties generally considered agreeable or useful. The leaves are aromatic and yield by distillation a fragrant volatile oil from the pellucid reservoirs. They are a good substitute for tea, and have been exported to China."

ADDITIONAL PLANTS USED FOR BEVERAGES AND FLAVORING

Bird's-Foot Fern, or Tea Fern, or Bird's-Foot Cliff Brake, Pellaea ornithopus. This fern, which grows in dry, often rocky situations from near sea level to six thousand feet, is often used as a beverage. It is native to California. The tea made by steeping the stems and leaves is tasty and somewhat aromatic. I recall once camping with gold prospectors in the Sierra Nevada Mountains. When we ran out of Oriental tea and could obtain no more, we used this as a substitute and found it agreeable. The miners spoke of it as rock-fern tea. The plants may be gathered at any time, for it is evergreen.

Douglas Spruce, or Douglas Fir, Pseudotsuga taxifolia. Native from California to Alaska. A tea made from the leaves of this magnificent tree is used by the Indians and sometimes by the whites.

Black Spruce, Picea mariana, and Red Spruce, Picea rubra, are common trees of southern Canada and the northern border of the United States, farther south in the mountains, whose young twigs and leaves are used in making the famous beverage, "spruce beer."

Hemlock, Tsuga canadensis, sometimes called Spruce Pine or

Hemlock Spruce, is a familiar tree in the north, extending south in the mountains to Alabama. A tea made from the leaves was used by the Indians, who apparently relished it. The lumbermen of Maine and Canada often resort to hemlock tea.

Desert Tea, or Teamsters' Tea, Ephedra sp. The Desert Tea is a shrub two to five feet high belonging to the joint-fir family, related to the junipers. There are three or four species very much alike, all growing in the dry regions of the Southwest. The leaves are reduced to mere bracts in whorls around the joints. A tea made by boiling the branches has long been used medicinally and has since become a popular beverage with both the Indians and the whites. It is sometimes called Mexican tea.

Sweet Gale, Myrica Gale. The Sweet Gale is a shrub two to four feet high growing in swamps and along ponds and lakes from Newfoundland to Alaska, south along the northern tier of states, and in the mountains to Virginia. The leaves have a pungent spicy odor, said to be valuable in giving a pleasant flavor to roasts.

Sweet Fern, Myrica asplenifolia, *Comptonia peregrina,* is a shrub one to three feet tall with fernlike leaves that when crushed give off a pleasing sweet fragrance. It grows on dry wooded hillsides and in neglected fields from Nova Scotia to Saskatchewan, south to North Carolina and Indiana. The leaves are reported to have been dried and used for tea during the Revolution. I have not tried it.

Sweet Bay, or Laurel Magnolia, Magnolia virginiana. The Sweet Bay is a shrub or small tree deciduous in the North, but evergreen in the South. Found in swamps east of the mountains from Massachusetts to Florida and westward to Arkansas and Texas. It is said that the leaves give flavor to roasts and gravy and perfume is made from the very fragrant flowers.

Purple or Water Avens, Geum rivale. This perennial plant grows in swamps and wet ground from Newfoundland to New Jersey, west to Alberta and Colorado. It has an aromatic root and an orange-purple flower about an inch across. The purplish root is used in making a beverage used as a substitute for cocoa. The plant is sometimes called Chocolate Root from its color and use.

Coffee Senna or Coffeeweed, Cassia occidentalis, is a native of tropical America and also of the old world. It has spread into the United States from Virginia to Kansas, south to Florida and Texas. The seeds, known as Magdad coffee, are roasted and used as a substitute for real coffee. Even in Africa it is used as a coffee substitute.

Chaparral Tea or Encinilla, Croton corymbulosus, grows from Western Texas to Arizona and south into Mexico. The flowering tops boiled in water make a very palatable drink. According to Havard, the colored soldiers of the southwestern frontier in our country preferred it to coffee.

The Appalachian Tea, or Evergreen Winterberry, Ilex glabra, grows from Nova Scotia to Florida, mainly near the coast. Dried leaves of this shrub are used as a substitute for Paraguay tea.

The Black Alder, or Winterberry, Ilex verticillata, is a shrub in swampy or wet places from Nova Scotia to Wisconsin, south to Florida and Missouri. Its leaves have also been used as a substitute for Oriental tea.

Wild Coffee, or Horse Gentian, Triosteum perfoliatum, also called Feverwort and Tinker's Weed, grows in rich woods and along fences and roadsides from Massachusetts to Nebraska, south to Alabama and Missouri. The dried and toasted berries are said to have been used by the early Pennsylvania Germans as a substitute for coffee and pronounced good.

Yerba Buena, Micromeria chamissonis, is an aromatic little plant of the Pacific Coast, belonging to the mint family. The dried leaves steeped in water make a palatable beverage.

Ground Ivy, Gill-over-the-Ground, Nepeta hederacea, *Glecoma hederacea*. Introduced from Europe, now extending from Newfoundland to Minnesota, south to Georgia, Tennessee, Kansas, and Colorado. It is said that the poor in England often use the leaves for making tea.

Garden or Lemon Balm, Melissa officinalis. This lemon-scented plant is a native of Europe. It was planted in gardens in this country and has now escaped from Maine to Georgia, west to Missouri. It is used in seasoning, to flavor liquors, and in medicines. It was once cultivated for these purposes.

Oswego Tea, or Bee Balm, Monarda didyma, is a fragrant plant with large heads of scarlet flowers. It may be found from Quebec to Michigan, south to Georgia and Tennessee. Tea is sometimes made from the leaves. Its strong mint flavor is sometimes employed in cooking. It frequently is mentioned in lists of pot and sweet herbs. The Wild Bergamot, Monarda fistulosa, and other species of Monarda have the same properties as the Oswego Tea.

Several additional plants belonging to the mint family were brought into this country from Europe for flavoring or other culinary purposes and have escaped. Among these we may mention the Common Horehound, Marrubium vulgare, Summer Savory, Satureja hortensis, Hyssop, Hyssopus officinalis, Marjoram, Origanum vulgare, probably the most abundant weed of the south-

ern Catskill Mountains, Wild Thyme, Thymus Serpyllum, probably the most abundant plant of the northern Catskill Mountains,
Horsemint, Mentha longifolia, and Field Mint, Mentha arvensis.
The Fragrant Giant Hyssop, Agastache Foeniculum, a native mint,
was used by the Indians of the Missouri valley for making a beverage and as a flavor in cooking.

Carolina Vanilla, or Vanilla Leaf, Trilisa odoratissima, is a plant
belonging to the thistle family. It grows in pine woods from Virginia to Florida, west to Louisiana. The crushed leaves have the
odor of vanilla. In Florida it is used to some extent commercially
by tobacconists to flavor smoking tobacco.

SUGARS AND GUMS

A GREAT many flowers have glands that secrete nectar, a sweet substance that bees gather and make into honey. Sugar is very common in the juices of fruits, and many plants and trees have sap that is sweet and, when boiled down, forms syrup or sugar. For quality, the peer of these is the Sugar Maple. Other plants and trees have a resinous substance with their sap. Some of these exude a gummy material that was chewed by the American Indians long before the advent of white people. A few have become popular with the whites and are even sold commercially. The gums are often mixed with sugar which dissolves in the chewing.

SUGAR PINE
Pinus lambertiana

THE Sugar Pine has thick brown bark with rough ridges, and five leaves or needles in a cluster. The leaves are two to four inches long. The cones are about six inches thick when opened, and thirteen inches long—sometimes longer. This is a common tree in the mountains of California and Oregon. John Muir, who admired beautiful trees, called it the Queen of the Sierras. When it is cut into or is injured, the exuding sap forms lumps of a sugary substance that is at first white but later turns brown. Muir thought this was the best of sweets. I have collected it fresh from the trees in the Sierra Nevada Mountains and found it sweet, but cared little for the resinous quality. However, many young people in the mountains seem to relish it. The sugar gradually dissolves, leaving a gummy substance which might serve for chewing gum.

BALSAM FIR, OR FIR TREE
Abies balsamea

THE Balsam Fir is a slender tree, sometimes reaching a height of eighty feet or even more; in the Arctic regions and on mountain tops it is small—often only a few feet high. The bark is smooth, warty with "balsam blisters." The leaves are dark green above, paler beneath, flat, nearly an inch long. The cones are two to four inches long, slightly more than an inch thick, standing erect from the upper side of the branches. The Balsam Fir ranges from Newfoundland and Labrador to Hudson Bay and Alberta, south to Massachusetts, Pennsylvania, and Iowa. It generally grows in damp woods and swamps, but is often found on mountain tops where evaporation goes on slowly.

Canada balsam is the resinous pitch that exudes from the trunks, forming lumps or blisters. When refined, it is used in the arts, especially in the mounting of microscope slides. Residents of the northern United States and Canada generally refer to it as "spruce gum." It has a resinous but not disagreeable flavor and was much used for chewing before the days of pleasantly flavored commercial chewing gums. In many places throughout its range, it was regularly bought and sold at the stores. For chewing purposes, it was generally molded into short sticks. People make a regular business of going into forests of Fir Trees, gathering the gum, and taking it to market. Robert Frost, the poet, describes one of these spruce-gum collectors:

> He showed me lumps of the scented stuff,
> Like uncut jewels, dull and rough.
> It comes to the market golden brown;
> But turns to pink between the teeth.[1]

I am told that the pitch of the White Pine, Pinus Strobus, is sometimes substituted for that of the Balsam, but it is too sticky and generally has to be boiled before using. The taste is rather disagreeable.

REED, OR COMMON REED GRASS

Phragmites communis

Phragmites Phragmites

THE Common Reed Grass is found in swamps, marshes, and wet places over almost the entire United States, southern Canada, and northern Mexico. It is also found in Europe and Asia. The culms,

[1] From "Mountain Interval" by Robert Frost. Used by special permission of the publishers, Henry Holt and Company.

or stalks, are stout, usually about an inch thick and five to twelve feet high. The leaves are about an inch wide and generally less than a foot long. The panicle is crowded and plumy, six inches to a foot long. From the large panicle and the size of the stalk, the plant is sometimes called Wild Broomcorn. It rarely produces seed, but spreads by its long horizontal rootstocks.

It is claimed that the Indians ate the roots of the reed, but they were fonder of the sugar it produced. Owing to accident or to the attack of insects which puncture the stem, a pasty substance exudes which hardens into gum. This the Indians collect and compress into balls to be eaten at pleasure. Dr. F. V. Coville says the Indians of Mohave Desert collect the plants in marshes, dry the stalks, grind them, and sift out the flour. This contains so much sugar that when placed near a fire, it swells, turns brown, and is then eaten like taffy. Of course this suggests roasted marshmallows. Dr. Palmer records a former practice of the Indians, who cut the reeds after the sugar had hardened, and placed them on blankets; after they had enough, the sugar was shaken off and dissolved in water, forming a sweet, nourishing drink.

SWEET GUM, OR RED GUM, OR BILSTED
Liquidambar Styraciflua

THE Sweet Gum, or Liquidambar, is a large forest tree found in damp woods on the coastal plain from Connecticut to Florida and Texas, north in the Mississippi valley to Missouri and Illinois. The gray bark is rough with corky ridges on the branches. The glossy green leaves are star-shaped, that is, with five to seven pointed lobes. In autumn, they turn various shades of red and purple. The fertile and sterile blossoms are in separate heads. The fertile ones, or those containing the pistils, are on long stems. They form a round, spinose ball nearly an inch and a half in diameter, containing numerous two-beaked capsules.

When the tree is injured, a pleasantly scented balsamic sap follows, which, when it hardens, forms a resin or gum. This gum, *copal-balsam* or *copalm,* is sometimes used as a substitute for storax. The storax of commerce comes from two other species of Liquidambar growing in southeastern Asia. According to Willard N. Clute, the resinous gum that our species produces is sometimes used as chewing gum.

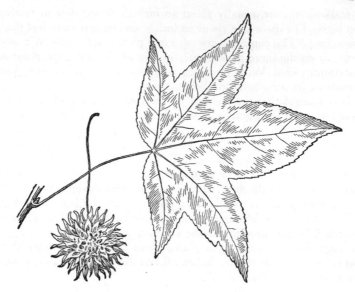

Sweet Gum (Liquidambar Styraciflua)

SUGAR MAPLE, OR SUGAR TREE, OR ROCK MAPLE
Acer saccharum

THE Sugar Maple is a large forest tree with upright branches, the lateral ones often wide-spreading. The bark of old trees is dark gray or brownish, scaly, channeled, forming wide flat ridges. Young trees have bark that is brownish gray and nearly smooth. The leaves have long stalks, or petioles. The blades are dark green above, paler beneath, about as wide as long, with five or occasionally three long-pointed irregular or coarse-toothed lobes. The yellow flowers appear just as the leaves are beginning to unfold, or often a few days earlier. They are long-stalked and drooping, making the tree conspicuous in bloom. The winged seeds, or samaras, are about an inch and a half long, and ripen in the autumn.

The Sugar Maple is found in rich woods, often on hillsides, from Newfoundland to Manitoba, south to Florida and Texas. The wood is very valuable for lumber, unusually so when it is of the bird's-eye and curly varieties. Many people consider the Sugar Maple to be the most valuable hardwood species in America. The autumn foliage is probably the most beautiful of all our trees, turning to bright yellow, orange, or even scarlet, so that it is especially desirable for roadside planting.

From the latter part of February to early April, depending on the latitude and season, holes are bored in maple trees into which spiles are driven. The cool clear sweet sap drips into pails or troughs and is then taken to the "sugarhouse" and boiled down into syrup or maple sugar, as the owner desires. On an average, about fifteen

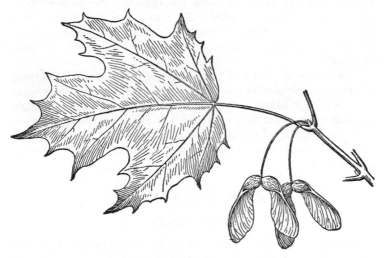

Sugar Maple (Acer saccharum)

quarts of the sap is required to make one pound of sugar. The amount varies greatly, however, the sap of some trees being much sweeter than that of others. Five or six pounds to a tree is about an average. Dr. Romeyn B. Hough made twenty-three pounds of sugar from one tree in a season without reboring, and thirty pounds from one tree has been recorded. I knew a very large tree on my father's farm that dripped eighteen gallons of sap in twenty-four hours. Clear days after frosty nights are best for sugar making.

The mere mention of maple sugar or maple syrup will call forth a chain of recollections to those who have lived in the country where this tree abounds. Some of the most pleasant recollections of my boyhood are connected with the making of these sweets—"tapping" the trees, gathering the sap, and boiling it down in the great pan in the sugarhouse in the woods. There was always enough weirdness about the whole process to excite our imaginations, especially in the evening as we sat around the foaming pan eating apples, telling stories, and occasionally drinking of the syrup which was becoming more and more sweet. Another pleasing pastime was making maple sugar taffy and "sugaring off"—pouring the melted candy on snow and eating it with a fork—a pastime often indulged in by older folks.

It is believed that the white people learned to make sugar from the maple tree from the Indians. Probably the earliest account was written about 1700. It tells how the Indians gathered the sap in bark or skin vessels, and boiled it down in a crude way. The report says that the sugar lacks the pleasing, delicate taste of cane sugar, and almost always has a burnt flavor. Now we consider it the finest of all sweets.

Along the south shore of Lake Superior in March, 1823, Henry Schoolcraft visited with the Indians while they were making sugar from the Rock Maple trees. Almost all the Indians of the neighborhood went to the maple forests. The sap was kept in large ox-hide vats, but the boiling was done in kettles. The Indians were so fond of the sugar that very little was preserved beyond the sugar making season.

BLACK SUGAR MAPLE
Acer nigrum

THIS is a large forest tree, very similar to the Sugar Maple—in fact, so much so that the average observer would take it for one and indeed many botanists consider it only a variety of the latter tree. Its bark is darker, and the leaves not so light beneath as those of the Sugar Maple; and the lobes are broader and shorter. The two species have much the same range, but the Black Sugar Maple does not extend so far south. It seems to be more common in the western part of its range. The sap is sweet and yields much sugar.

RED MAPLE, OR SWAMP MAPLE
Acer rubrum

THE Red Maple is a large forest tree with light gray bark, nearly smooth or somewhat flaky in old trees. The twigs have a reddish tinge—often quite red where the growth is rapid. The leaves have a heart-shaped base, three to five irregular toothed lobes which are sharp at the base. The leaves are smooth and dark green above, very pale beneath. The red or yellowish odorous blossoms in lateral clusters make this tree a pleasing feature of the landscape in early spring. The winged fruits are small—rarely more than an inch long —and drop early. The foliage turns crimson in autumn.

The Red Maple usually grows in swamps and low ground from Nova Scotia to Manitoba south to Florida and Texas. It produces much sap, which is less sweet than that of the Sugar Maple.

SILVER MAPLE, OR SOFT OR WHITE MAPLE

Acer saccharinum

THE Silver Maple is a large forest tree with light gray, flaky bark and wide-spreading branches. The leaves are deeply five-lobed, green above, silvery white beneath. The flowers, usually pale yellow, appear in early spring. The winged fruits are large—two inches or more long—and mature early.

The Silver Maple is generally found in low grounds and along streams from New Brunswick to Florida, west to South Dakota and Oklahoma. It is rather scarce in the mountains. The sap produces sugar, but it is not so very sweet.

BOX ELDER, OR ASH-LEAVED MAPLE

Acer Negundo

THE Ash-Leaved Maple is a wide-spreading forest tree found along streams, lake shores, and in lowlands from Maine to Manitoba, south to Florida and Mexico. It is rare along the Atlantic coast but is frequently planted and often escapes. The leaves have three to five leaflets which are slightly lobed, toothed, or entire. They do not resemble those of a maple tree. The wood is soft, weak, and light. The sap produces sugar but is less sweet than that of the Sugar Maple. In Illinois and elsewhere, groves of this tree have been planted for making sugar and syrup. The tree is easily grown.

The Sugarbush, Rhus ovata, which grows on dry hills, especially along the mountains in southern California, has glossy evergreen leaves and stiff panicles of flowers. The berries are red. Dr. Jepson says, "The sweetish waxen covering of the berries is used by the native tribes for sugar."

SKELETON WEED

Lygodesmia juncea

THIS is a stiff erect perennial, closely related to the Wild Lettuce. The much-branched stems grow eight to sixteen inches high. The lower leaves are an inch or two long and very narrow. The upper leaves are similar but much smaller, often reduced to narrow scales. The pink flower heads, composed of five flowers, are at the ends of the branches.

The Skeleton Weed is found from Wisconsin and Minnesota to Montana, south to Missouri and New Mexico. The plants are often infested with small round galls which contain much gum. According to M. R. Gilmore, this plant was used by the Indians of the Missouri River valley for producing chewing gum. He says: "The stems were gathered and cut into pieces to cause the juice to exude. When this hardened, it was collected and used for chewing."

COMPASS PLANT, OR PILOTWEED

Silphium laciniatum

THE Compass Plant, often called Rosinweed, is a rough, coarse perennial, six to twelve feet high. The large basal leaves are cut almost to the midrib, forming numerous narrow lobes. The alternate, sessile stem leaves have their edges vertical, generally pointing north and south. The yellow flower heads are three or four inches across and resemble those of a Wild Sunflower.

The Compass Plant is found on prairies from Ohio to South Dakota, south to Alabama, Louisiana, and Texas. The stalk is very resinous, and according to M. R. Gilmore the Indian children gather chewing gum from the upper parts of the stem, where the gum exudes, forming large lumps.

MUSHROOMS

EDIBLE mushrooms are so numerous, and so many popular books have recently appeared on the subject, that I will pass them by with mere mention. From spring until late autumn, the student of mushrooms can usually find edible species growing in abundance unless the season is too dry. Within ten miles of New York City, the writer has collected and eaten wild mushrooms every month in the year. This cannot be done every year, however, for during very cold winters, I should not expect to find them from January to April. Several species are apt to be abundant in November and December.

Mushrooms should be studied and learned like flowering plants. When a species is in doubt, it should not be eaten. I have collected, prepared, and eaten more than sixty species of edible fungi. This is only a beginning, however, for hundreds are known to be edible.

Often in camping in the woods, I have made use of mushrooms, frying them with bacon or stewing them to use for soups, and find that they give splendid relief from the monotony of canned goods.

The following species I have found to be excellent in quality and flavor.

Meadow Mushroom	*Agaricus campestris*
Field Mushroom	*Agaricus arvensis*
Red Hypholoma	*Hypholoma perplexum*
Shaggy-Mane	*Coprinus comatus*
Ink Cap	*Coprinus atramentarius*
Glistening Coprinus	*Coprinus micaceus*
Parasol Mushroom	*Lepiota procera*
Honey Mushroom	*Armillaria mellea*
Root Mushroom	*Collybia radicata*
Velvet Collybia	*Collybia velutipes*
Elm Mushroom	*Pleurotus ulmarius*
Oyster Mushroom	*Pleurotus ostreatus*
Delicious Milky Mushroom	*Lactarius deliciosus*
Green Russula	*Russula virescens*
Chanterelle	*Cantharellus cibarius*
Fairy Ring	*Marasmius oreades*

Pluteus	*Pluteus cervinus*
Pine Cone Mushroom	*Strobilomyces strobilaceus*
Beefsteak Mushroom	*Fistulina hepatica*
Sulphus Mushroom	*Polyporus sulphureus*
Coral Fungus	*Hydnum coralloides*
Bear's-Head	*Hydnum caput-ursi*
Giant Puffball	*Lycoperdon giganteum*
Beaker Puffball	*Lycoperdon cyathiforme*
Edible Morel	*Morchella esculenta*

All species of puffballs are good when fresh, that is when pure white within. All mushrooms should be eaten fresh.

EDIBLE PLANTS

of Northeastern United States and Eastern Canada, west to Mississippi River

Wild Fruits

SCIENTIFIC AND COMMON NAMES	CHARACTERISTICS	RANGE	IN SEASON	PAGE
Amelanchier Bartramiana (Oblong-Fruited Juneberry)	Shrub 3–8 ft. high, fr. dark purple ⅓ in. in diam.	N.Y. and n.	July and Aug.	39
Amelanchier canadensis (Juneberry)	Small tree, smooth bark, fr. dark red ¼–⅓ in. in diam.	N.S. to Ont. s. to Fla. and La.	June to Aug.	37
Amelanchier intermedia (Sugar Pear)	Shrub or small tree, fr. dark purple with bloom ⅓ in. in diam.	Eastern U.S.	July and Aug.	39
Asimina triloba (Papaw)	Small tree, lvs. large, entire fr. 4 in. long, 1½ in. thick, yellowish green	N.J. to Mich. and Nebr. s. to Fla. and Tex.	Sept. and Oct.	9
Berberis vulgaris (European Barberry)	Shrub 8 ft. high, fls. yellow, fr. oblong, scarlet, ½ in. long	Eastern and middle states	Summer to autumn	11
Celtis crassifolia (Rough - Leaved Hackberry)	Tree, lvs. downy, elmlike, fr. purplish black ⅓ in. in diam., 1-seeded	Eastern U.S. w. to Plains	Autumn and winter	5
Celtis occidentalis (Hackberry)	Tree, lvs. smooth, elmlike, fr. dark brown ⅓ in. in diam., 1-seeded	Eastern U.S. w. to plains	Autumn and winter	3
Chiogenes hispidula (Creeping Snowberry)	Creeping evergreen shrub, lvs. small, berries white ½ in. long	Lab. to B.C., s. to N.C., Mich. and Minn.	Aug. and Sept.	76

235

SCIENTIFIC AND COMMON NAMES	CHARACTERISTICS	RANGE	IN SEASON	PAGE
Opuntia Rafinesquii (Western Prickly Pear)	Cactus, spreading, jointed, flat, prickly, fr. 1–2 in. long, red	Mich. and Minn., s. to Tex.	Summer and autumn	63
Opuntia vulgaris (Eastern Prickly Pear)	Cactus, spreading, flat, jointed, prickly, fr. 1–2 in. long, red	Mass. to Fla. and Ala. near coast	Summer and autumn	61
Passiflora lutea (Yellow Passion Flower)	Vine, tendril climbing, fls. yellow, fr. ½ in. in diam., purple	Pa. to Ill. and Kans., s. to Fla. and Tex.	Aug. to Oct.	60
Physalis ixocarpa (Tomatillo)	Branching annual, fr. purple, in a husk (calyx)	N.Y. to Tex. and Calif.	Aug. to Oct.	80
Physalis pubescens (Ground Cherry)	Branching annual, fr. in husk, yellow, ½ in. in diam.	N.Y. and Pa. s. and w.	Aug. to Oct.	79
Podophyllum peltatum (May Apple)	Plant 15 in. high, 2 lvs., fr. pulpy, yellow, ovoid, 2 in. long	Que. to Fla. w. to plains	July and Aug.	13
Prunus alleghaniensis (Porter's Plum)	Shrub or small tree, fr. dark purple with bloom ½ in. in diam.	Conn. to Pa.	Aug. to Oct.	46
Prunus americana (Wild Plum)	Small tree, slightly thorny, fr. 1 in. in diam., red or yellow	Conn. to Mont. s. to Fla., Tex. and N.M.	Aug. to Oct.	40
Prunus Avium (Sweet Cherry)	Large tree, fr. in umbels, black or dark red, sweet	Eastern U.S.	July	46
Prunus Cerasus (Sour Cherry)	Tree, fr. in umbels, round, red or dark brown, sour	Eastern U.S.	July	48
Prunus hortulana (Wild Goose Plum)	Small tree, spreading, fr. bright red	W. Va. to Kans. s. to Miss. and Tex.	July and Aug.	43
Prunus maritima (Beach Plum)	Shrub 4 ft. high, fr. round, ¾–1 in. across, purple	N.B. to Va. near coast	Aug. and Sept.	44

SCIENTIFIC AND COMMON NAMES	CHARACTERISTICS	RANGE	IN SEASON	PAGE
Vaccinium Vitis-Idaea (Cowberry)	Low shrub, 4–8 in., creeping, fr. red ⅓ in. in diam.	Mass. and N.Y. n. to Arctic Am.	July to Sept.	70
Viburnum alnifolium (Hobblebush)	All viburnums have opposite leaves and clustered, 1-seeded fruits; shrub, branches spreading, lvs. large, fr. clustered, purple	N.B. to Ont. s. to Pa. and Tenn.	Aug. to Oct.	84
Viburnum cassinoides (Withe-Rod)	Shrub 5–10 ft. high, clustered fr. blue-black	N.J. to Man. s. to Ga. and Ala.	Aug. to Oct.	86
Viburnum Lentago (Nannyberry)	Shrub or small tree, fr. blue-black	Que. to Hudson Bay, s. to N.J., Ind. and Kans.	Aug. to Oct.	85
Viburnum nudum (Larger Withe-Rod)	Shrub 5–15 ft. high, fr. blue-black with bloom	Conn. to Ky. s. to Fla. and Tex.	Aug. to Oct.	86
Viburnum Opulus (Cranberry Tree)	Shrub 8 ft. high, fr. bright red, clustered	Nfld. to B.C., s. to N.J., Ia. and Ore.	Sept. to Nov.	84
Viburnum pauciflorum (Pimbina)	Spreading shrub 3–5 ft. high; fr. light red	Nfld. to B.C., s. to N. J., Ia. and Ore.	Aug. to Oct.	85
Viburnum prunifolium (Black Haw)	Shrub or small tree, fr. blue-black with bloom	Conn., Mich. and Kans., s. to Ga. and Tex.	Sept. to Dec.	86
Vitis aestivalis (Summer Grape)	Woody vine, fr. in dense clusters, blue-black ⅓ in. in diam., lvs. rusty beneath	N.H. to Fla. w. to Kans. and Tex.	Aug. to Oct.	55
Vitis bicolor (Blue Grape)	Similar, lvs. whitish beneath, fr. ⅓ in. in diam.	N.H. to N.C. w. to Ill. and Tenn.	Sept. to Nov.	56
Vitis cordifolia (Chicken Grape)	Vine, high-climbing, lvs. green beneath, fr. black ¼ in. in diam.	Pa. to Nebr. s. to Fla. and Tex.	Sept. to Dec.	56

Edible Seeds and Seed Pods

Salad Plants and Potherbs

Edible Roots and Tubers

Beverage and Flavoring Plants

Sugars and Gums

EDIBLE PLANTS

of Southern United States

Wild Fruits

SCIENTIFIC AND COMMON NAMES	CHARACTERISTICS	RANGE	IN SEASON	PAGE
Amelanchier canadensis (Juneberry)	Small tree, smooth bark, fr. ¼ to ⅓ in. in diam.	N.S. to Ont., s. to Fla. and Tex.	June and July	37
Annona glabra (Pond Apple)	Tree, evergreen, lvs. oval, leathery, fr. 4 in. long	Florida and Bahama Is.	Summer and autumn	11
Asimina triloba (Papaw)	Small tree, lvs. large, entire, fr. 4 in. long, 1½ in. thick, yellow-green	N. J. to Mich. and Nebr., s. to Fla. and Tex.	Summer and autumn	9
Berberis canadensis (American Barberry)	Shrub 2 to 4 ft. high, spiny, fr. oval, scarlet	Mts. of Va. s. and w.	Aug. to Oct.	12
Bumelia lycioides (Southern Buckthorn)	Shrub, 1 to 3 ft. high, berry black, ⅓ in. long, 1-seeded	Va. to Ky., s. to Fla. and Tex.	Summer to frost	52
Celtis mississippiensis (Southern Hackberry)	Large tree, bark warty, fr. dark brown, ¼ in. in diam.	Southern states	Autumn and winter	5
Condalia obovata (Purple Haw)	Shrub or small tree, spiny, fr. ¼ in. in diam., black	Texas and Mexico	Summer and autumn	53
Crataegus aestivalis (May Haw)	Small tree, spiny, fr. red, ½ in. in diam.	Southern states	May to July	40
Diospyros texana (Black Persimmon)	Small tree, bark smooth, fr. black, 1 in. in diam.	Texas and Mexico	Late summer and autumn	79

SCIENTIFIC AND COMMON NAMES	CHARACTERISTICS	RANGE	IN SEASON	PAGE
Podophyllum pelta-tum (May Apple)	Plant, 15 in. high, 2 lvs., fr. pulpy, yellow, ovoid, 2 in. long	Que. to Fla., w. to Plains	July and Aug.	13
Prunus americana (Wild Plum)	Small tree, slightly thorny, fr. 1 in. in diam., red or yellow	Conn. to Mont., s. to Fla., Tex., and N.M.	July to Sept.	40
Prunus angustifo-lia (Chickasaw Plum)	Shrub or small tree, fr. red or yellow with bloom	Del. to Fla., w. to Kans. and Tex.	July and Aug.	45
Prunus hortulana (Wild Goose Plum)	Small tree, spreading, fr. bright red	W.Va. to Kans., s. to Miss. and Tex.	July and Aug.	43
Prunus serotina (Black Wild Cherry)	Large tree, fr. in racemes, black, ⅓ in. in diam.	N.S. to Dak., s. to Fla. and Tex.	Aug. and Sept.	48
Prunus virginiana (Choke Cherry)	Shrub or small tree, fr. racemes, red or brown, ⅓ in. in diam.	Can. to Gulf, Atlantic to Pacific	Aug. and Sept.	49
Pyrus angustifolia (Narrow-Leaved Crab Apple)	Small tree, lvs. oblong, toothed, fr. 1 in. in diam.	N.J. to Kans., s. to Fla. and La.	Oct. to Dec.	32
Reynosia latifolia (Darling Plum)	Tree, small evergreen, fr. oval black, ¾ in. long	Fla. and Keys	Summer and autumn	53
Rhamnus carolini-ana (Indian Cherry)	Shrub or small tree, bark gray, fr. round, black, ⅖ in. in diam.	Va. to Fla., w. to Kans. and Tex.	Autumn	51
Rubus occidentalis (Black Raspberry)	Shrub, prickly glaucous, fr. purple-black	Que. to Ont., s. to Ga. and Mo.	June to Aug.	25
Rubus odoratus (Purple-Flowering Raspberry)	Shrubby, unarmed, fls. purple, fr. red, depressed	N.S. to Ga., w. to Mich. and Tenn.	July and Aug.	23
Rubus procumbens (Dewberry)	Shrubby, trailing, fr. black, large, few drupelets	Me. to Ont., s. to Va., La., and Okla.	July and Aug.	30

Edible Nuts

SCIENTIFIC AND COMMON NAMES	CHARACTERISTICS	RANGE	IN SEASON	PAGE
Quercus prinoides (Scrub Chestnut Oak)	Shrub or small tree, lvs. whitish beneath, chestnutlike, acorn sessile	Me. to Minn., s. to Ala. and Tex.	Sept. to Nov.	112
Quercus prinus (Rock Chestnut Oak)	Large tree, lvs. chestnutlike, cup thin, acorn large	Me. to s. Ont., s. to Ala. and Tenn.	Sept. to Nov.	112

Edible Seeds and Seed Pods

Amaranthus hybridus (Red Amaranth)	Annual weed, 4 ft. high, root red, seeds small, black shining	Over most of N.A.	Summer and autumn	129, 163
Arundinaria gigantea (Large Cane)	Shrubby grass, 10 to 25 ft. high, on river banks	Va. to Mo., s. to Fla. and La.	Summer and autumn	129
Brassica nigra (Black Mustard)	Annual, 2 to 5 ft. high, fls. yellow, pods ½ in. long, seeds brown	U.S. and s. Can.	Summer and autumn	116
Gleditsia triacanthos (Honey Locust)	Large tree with branching thorns, pod brown, flat, 1 ft. long twisted	N.Y. to Fla. w. to Mich., Kans. and Tex.	Autumn	121
Lupinus perennis (Wild Lupine)	Erect perennial, pea-like fls., blue in spikes, pods 1½ in. long	Me. to Minn., s. to Fla. and Tex.	Summer and early autumn	129
Medicago lupulina (Black Medic)	Cloverlike, fls. yellow, pod twisted	Over most of U.S.	Summer	129
Nelumbo lutea (American Lotus)	Water plant, fls. large, pale yellow, seeds acornlike	Mass. to Minn., s. to Fla. and Tenn. (rare)	Autumn to winter	115
Phaseolus polystachyus (Wild Bean)	Perennial, vine, leaflets 3, fls. purple, pods 2 in. long	Conn. to Nebr., s. to Fla. and Tex.	Autumn	122

Salad Plants

SCIENTIFIC AND COMMON NAMES	CHARACTERISTICS	RANGE	IN SEASON	PAGE
Stellaria media (Chickweed)	Annual, tufted, weak, lvs. opposite, fls. white	Throughout U.S.	Spring	146
Taraxacum officinale (Dandelion)	Stemless herb, basal, tufted, toothed leaves	Nearly throughout U.S.	Spring	159
Trifolium pratense (Red Clover)	Common field crop, lvs. three, fl. heads purple	Nearly throughout U.S.	Spring	165
Ulmus fulva (Slippery Elm)	Tree, rough bark, lvs. rough, inner bark slippery	Que. to N.D., s. to Fla. and Tex.	Spring	163
Uvularia perfoliata (Bellwort)	Herb, forked, 1 ft. high, lvs. perfoliate	Que. to Ont., s. to Fla. and Miss.	Spring	162
Valerianella radiata (Beaked Corn Salad)	Annual, forked, 10 in. high, fls. white	Mass. to Minn., s. to Fla. and Tex.	Spring and summer	158
Viola palmata (Early Blue Violet)	Stemless, lvs. 5- to 9-lobed, fls. violet	Mass. to Minn., s. to Ga.	April and May	165

Edible Roots and Tubers

Acorus Calamus (Calamus Root)	Plant 2 ft. high, lvs. sword-shaped, root pungent	N.S. to Minn., s. to Fla. and Tex.	All seasons	173
Allium canadense (Meadow Garlic)	Onionlike, 1 ft high, umbel bulb-bearing	N.B. to Fla., w. to Minn., Colo., and Tex.	Spring	176
Allium cernuum (Nodding Wild Onion)	Onionlike, scape angular, 1 to 2 ft. high, fls. pink	N.Y. to S.C., w. to Calif.	Spring	175
Amphicarpa monoica (Hog Peanut)	Slender vine, 3 leaflets, pods pea-like, 1 in. long	N.B. to Fla., w. to Man., Nebr. and La.	Spring and autumn	189

Beverage and Flavoring Plants

Sugars and Gums

EDIBLE PLANTS

from the Mississippi River to the Rocky Mountains

Wild Fruits

SCIENTIFIC AND COMMON NAMES	CHARACTERISTICS	RANGE	IN SEASON	PAGE
Amelanchier alnifolia (Northwestern Juneberry)	Shrub, 4–7 ft. high, fr. purple with bloom ⅓ in. in diam.	Ont. to B.C., s. to Nebr. and Calif.	Summer	38
Asimina triloba (Papaw)	Small tree, lvs. large, entire, fr. 4 in. long, 1½ in. thick, yellow-green	N.J. to Mich., Nebr., s. to Fla. and Tex.	Autumn	9
Celtis crassifolia (Rough-Leaved Hackberry)	Tree, lvs. elmlike, downy, fr. purplish black, ⅓ in. in diam., 1-seeded	E. U.S., w. to plains	Autumn and winter	5
Celtis occidentalis (Hackberry)	Tree, lvs. smooth, elmlike, bark rough, fr. brown, ⅓ in. in diam.	E. U.S., w. to plains	Autumn and winter	3
Chiogenes hispidula (Creeping Snowberry)	Creeping evergreen shrub, lvs. small, berries white, ½ in. long	N. U.S. and Can.	Summer and autumn	76
Cornus canadensis (Bunchberry)	Shrubby, 3–8 in. high, lvs. whorled at top, fr. red in cluster	Nfld. to Alaska, s. to N.J., W.Va., Colo., and Calif.	Summer	89
Diospyros virginiana (Persimmon)	Tree, bark dark, rough, fr. orange, 1–1½ in. in diam.	Conn. to Ia. and Kans., s. to Fla. and Tex.	Autumn and winter	77
Elaeagnus argentea (Silverberry)	Shrub, 6–10 ft. high, lvs. silvery, fr. ⅓ in. long	Dak. and Mont., n. into Can.	Late summer and autumn	66

Edible Nuts

Edible Seeds and Seed Pods

SCIENTIFIC AND COMMON NAMES	CHARACTERISTICS	RANGE	IN SEASON	PAGE
Zizania aquatica (Wild Rice)	Tall grass in swamps, grain dark, ½ to 1 in. long	N.B. to Man., s. to Fla. and Tex.	Summer and autumn	113

Salad Plants and Potherbs

Amaranthus hybridus (Slender Pigweed)	Annual, 4 ft. high, roots red, seeds black	Can. to tropics	Spring and summer	163
Amaranthus retroflexus (Green Amaranth)	Annual, stout, 3 to 6 ft. high, roots red, seeds black	U.S. generally	Spring to autumn	143
Arctuum minus (Common Burdock)	Biennial, lvs. large, purple fls. forming burs	Over much of U.S.	May to Aug.	166
Asclepias syriaca (Milkweed)	Perennial, lvs. opposite, fls. pale purple, fr. beaked pod	N.B. to Sask., s. to Va. and Kans.	May and June	155
Barbarea vulgaris (Winter Cress)	Tufted erect, lvs. smooth, fls. yellow, 1 to 2 ft. high	Lab. to Va., w. to Coast	Mar. to May	151
Caltha palustris (Marsh Marigold)	Fleshy plants, in swamps, stems hollow, fls. yellow	Nfld. to N.C., w. to Sask and Nebr.	Apr. and May	146
Capsella Bursa-pastoris (Shepherd's-Purse)	Annual, fls. white, 1 ft. high, lvs. mostly basal, mustard flavor	World-wide	Apr. and May	164
Cardamine pennsylvanica (Pennsylvania Bitter Cress)	Annual, 1 ft. tall, lvs. deep cut, fls. white, wet grounds	Nfld. to Minn., Mont., s. to Fla., Tenn., and Kans.	May to Aug.	152
Chenopodium album (Lamb's Quarter)	Weed, annual, 2 to 6 ft. tall, branched, fls. small greenish	Over N.A. and Europe	May to Sept.	140
Cichorium Intybus (Chicory)	Perennial, 1 to 4 ft. tall, lvs. basal, chiefly, fls. blue	N.S. to Minn., s. to Fla. and Kans., West Coast	Apr. and May	158

Edible Roots and Tubers

Beverage and Flavoring Plants

SCIENTIFIC AND COMMON NAMES	CHARACTERISTICS	RANGE	IN SEASON	PAGE
Rhus trilobata (Squaw Bush)	Shrub, smooth, 2–5 ft. high, fr. in clustered spikes, red	Ill. to Tex., w. to Coast	Summer and autumn	213
Sassafras variifolium (Sassafras)	Tree, twigs green, bark spicy aromatic	Mass., Mich., Ia., and Kans., s. to Fla. and Tex.	Entire year	205
Triosteum perfoliatum (Horse Gentian)	Herb, 2 to 3 ft. tall, lvs. clasping, fr. orange	Mass. to Nebr., s. to Ala. and Mo.	Late summer and autumn	222

Sugars and Gums

Abies balsamea (Balsam Fir)	Tree, evergreen, lvs. linear, cones erect, 2–4 in. long	Nfld. to Hudson Bay and Sask., s. to Mass., Pa., and Ia.	Entire year	225
Acer Negundo (Box Elder)	Tree (maple), lvs. opposite compound, fr. winged	Me. to Man., s. to Fla. and Mex.	Feb. to Apr.	231
Acer rubrum (Red Maple)	Forest tree, gray bark, lvs. sharp-lobed, fr. small	N.S. to Man., s. to Fla. and Tex.	Feb. to Apr.	230
Acer saccharinum (Silver Maple)	Large tree, gray bark, lvs. deep-lobed, fr. large	N.B. to Fla., w. to S.D. and Okla.	Feb. to Apr.	231
Acer saccharum (Sugar Maple)	Forest tree, bark dark gray, scaly, lobes of lvs. long-pointed	Nfld. to Man., s. to Fla. and Tex.	Feb. to Apr.	228
Lygodesmia juncea (Skeleton Weed)	Perennial, stem stiff, branched, rushlike, 8–16 in. high, hds. few-fld.	Wis. and Minn., to Mont., s. to Mo. and N.M.	Summer	232
Phragmites communis (Reed Grass)	Coarse grass, 5–12 ft. high, panicle plumelike, swampy ground	Throughout U.S. and s. Can.	Summer	226

SCIENTIFIC AND COMMON NAMES	CHARACTERISTICS	RANGE	IN SEASON	PAGE
Silphium lacinia-tum (Compass Plant)	Rough perennial, 6–10 ft. high, lvs. edges vertical, fl. head large	Ohio to S.D., s. to Ala., La., and Tex.	Summer	232

EDIBLE PLANTS
of the Rocky Mountains and Pacific States

Wild Fruits

SCIENTIFIC AND COMMON NAMES	CHARACTERISTICS	RANGE	IN SEASON	PAGE
Amelanchier alnifolia (Northwestern Juneberry)	Shrub, 4–7 ft. high, fr. purple, with bloom ⅓ in. in diam.	Ont. to Nebr., w. to Br. Col. and Cal.	Summer	38
Arctostaphylos Manzanita (Manzanita)	Wide spreading shrubs, bark smooth, brownish red, fr. red	Pacific Coast	Summer	90
Berberis aquifolium (Oregon Grape)	Shrub, 5 ft. high, spreading, lvs. evergreen, fr. dark blue, clustered	Rocky Mts. to Coast	Autumn	88
Berberis haematocarpa (Red-Fruited Barberry)	Shrub, evergreen, 5–10 ft. high, leaflets 5, fr. blood-red	N.M. and Ariz.	Summer	89
Celtis reticulata (Western Hackberry)	Tree, 20–40 ft. high, lvs. small, unequal at base, fr. brown	Colo. to w. Tex., w. to Calif.	Autumn	5
Cereus giganteus (Giant Cactus)	Our largest cactus, columnar or with 1 or 2 br., 5 to 35 ft. high, fr. red	Arizona	Autumn	89
Condalia obovata (Purple Haw)	Spiny shrub or small tree, lvs. leathery, fr. black, ¼ in. in diam.	Tex. and Mexico	Summer	53
Crataegus rivularis (Western Black Hawthorn)	Shrub or small tree, spines ½ in. long, fr. nearly black	Rocky Mtn. States	Autumn	40

Edible Nuts

Edible Seeds and Seed Pods

SCIENTIFIC AND COMMON NAMES	CHARACTERISTICS	RANGE	IN SEASON	PAGE
Amaranthus blitoides (Prostrate Amaranth)	Annual weed, spreading, seeds, small, black	Me. to N.J., w. to Pacific	Summer and autumn	129
Amaranthus hybridus (Red Amaranth)	Annual weed, 4 ft. high, root red, seed small black shining	Over most of N.A.	Summer and autumn	129
Avena fatua (Wild Oat)	Grass, 2 to 3 ft. tall, similar to common oats	Wis. and Ill., w. to Coast	Summer	128
Brassica nigra (Black Mustard)	Annual, 2 to 5 ft. fls. yellow, pod ½ in. long	U.S. and s. Can.	Summer and autumn	116
Elymus condensatus (Rye Grass)	Tufted grass, 3–6 ft. tall, spike 6–12 in. long	Minn. to Colo. and N.M., w. to Pacific	Autumn	128
Elymus triticoides (Wild Wheat)	Grass, culms smooth, 2–4 ft. tall, spike 4–8 in. long	Minn. to Colo. s. and w. to Pacific	Summer and autumn	128
Helianthus annuus (Sunflower)	Annual, 3–6 ft. tall, rough, fl. heads 3–6 in. broad	Minn. to Tex., w. to Coast	Autumn	127
Linum Lewisii (Blue Flax)	Perennial, slender, 1–2 ft. high, lvs. linear, crowded, fls. blue	Wis. to Tex., w. to Alaska and Calif.	Summer and autumn	130
Madia sativa (Chile Tarweed)	Annual, erect, robust, 1–4 ft. high, ill-scented, fls. yellow	Pacific Coast	Summer and autumn	130
Medicago lupulina (Black Medic)	Cloverlike, spreading, fls. yellow, pod twisted	Over most of U.S.	Summer and autumn	129
Nymphaea polysepala (Indian Pond Lily)	Plant, aquatic, pistil 1, compound, fls. yellow	Alaska to Calif. and Col.	Summer and autumn	116
Oryzopsis hymenoides (Indian Millet)	Grass, tufted, 1–2 ft. tall, panicle, 3–6 in. long	Ia. to Tex., w. to Wash. and Calif.	Summer and autumn	128

Salad Plants and Potherbs

Edible Roots and Tubers

Beverage and Flavoring Plants

GENERAL INDEX

Synonyms in Italics

305